KU-362-307

# Contents

DISCARDED FROM STOCK

STAFFORDSHIRE UNIVERSITY LIBRARY

04334676

# Foreword

This research report was commissioned by the Health Education Authority (HEA), as part of a wider programme of research to coincide with the United Nation's International Year of the Family in 1994. The research programme aimed to provide a greater insight into the mechanisms of family health, thus informing parents and professionals about effective ways of taking forward health promotion work with young people.

The HEA has a national remit for health education in England. It advises the Secretary of State, organises national health education campaigns and works with health service commissioners and providers to help them implement national health promotion targets. Good research-based evidence is key to improving health and healthcare, and for this reason the HEA bases its campaigns on thorough needs assessment and evaluation.

Over the last decade the HEA has worked with parents and professionals to improve and promote the health of children. Emphasis is put on offering appropriate support to parents in the complex and sometimes stressful task of promoting the health and education of children and young people. Projects have focused on increasing the uptake of child immunisations, reduction of child accidents, and advice and support for pregnant mothers and first time parents. We have also produced training materials for those working in parenting education and initiated inter-agency collaboration through workshops, seminars and the provision of resource databases. The research reported on here forms part of the on-going needs assessment in the area of parent and child health. Previous initiatives include a report on health promotion for children under 5 and a review of the literature assessing the effectiveness of health promotion interventions on infant mortality and morbidity.

The HEA encounters a constant demand from health professionals to provide materials to support parents, yet appropriate health education messages, and the style and manner in which they are relayed, are increasingly open to question. This report highlights the importance of recognising the environmental, social and economic constraints which influence parental behaviour and shows how parental roles and needs change as children grow and develop. It also stresses that there is no 'blueprint' defining the ideal parent. Different parents adopt different parenting styles which may work to equal effect; individual styles need to be respected and supported. Such messages are particularly important in an environment where parents are probably under more intense pressure from the media and a range of professionals than at any other time, to create a healthy, nurturing and moral environment for their young.

A full list of publications forming part of the HEA Family Health Research Programme may be found at the end of the report in Appendix D.

Kathy Elliott

# Executive summary

### 1. *Aims of the study*

- To investigate lay understandings of mental health and mental ill health.
- To examine lay views about emotional support. How do people define it and where do people get it from?
- To build a picture of how decisions and behaviour relevant to mental health are enacted and prioritised within the fabric of family and domestic life.
- To examine to what extent material differences facilitate patterns of emotional support and the use of informal and formal resources.

### 2. *Method*

Qualitative studying using in-depth interviews. Interviews were conducted with parents and teenage children in 45 families. A spread of family types was interviewed, working-class, middle-class, single and dual parents.

### 3. *Results*

**Constraints on the discussion of mental health**
Mental health is an inherently personal issue, views and experiences pertaining to mental health are therefore difficult to elicit.

**Definitions of mental health**
Respondents had a great deal of trouble locating what they felt to be appropriate definitions of mental health. Some respondents placed mental health in the body: 'it's something to do with the brain.' Unlike physical health, mental health tended to remain in the background; unacknowledged until something went wrong.

**Causes of mental health**
Major life events were cited as the predominant cause of poor mental health: divorce, bereavement, unemployment and financial difficulties. Few respondents alluded to genetic causation.

**Maintaining mental health**
Strategies employed by respondents to maintain good mental health included:

- Self-reliance – striving for autonomy.
  'you have to be strong in yourself and try to get over it yourself'.
- Giving yourself space and time.
- Seeking professional help (psychiatrist).
- Support/advice from family and friends.

- Cognitive strategies – optimism – being 'aware' of problems.
- Moral responsibility.
- Sport and stress-reducing activities (important for men).

**Emotional support**
A number of accounts (from across all family types) expressed an ambivalence about intimacy and confiding. A close confiding relationship, especially amongst teenage girls, helped maintain a sense of well-being – but was not always made use of when problems arose. Then someone who they felt would 'take their problems seriously' was sought.

A number of respondents explained how they felt comfortable confiding in people they knew to have suffered their own problems/depression. The provision of written information on mental health issues was seen as useful for a variety of reasons. People found it empowering, reassuring, helping to normalise the way they felt.

**Emotional support and professionals**
GPs were not the first source of emotional support for most repondents – though more men than women used the GP for this purpose. There was a clear preference for lay social support, as opposed to medical support, in dealing with emotional problems.

**Mental health and family relationships and conflict**
A certain level of conflict within families is seen as important, though it was acknowledged that long-term conflict between partners could be damaging.

**Communication**
Men found communication harder than women. Women worried that men and male teenagers were bottling things up. Effective communication appears to be linked to family closeness.

Family relationships between adults and children and their parents, proved impossible to categorise – since the shape and form of negotiation was so diverse. There are, however, differences in the way men and women experience conflict and how this is expressed and communicated within the family.

**Babies, toddlers and mental health**

- The birth of a child brings in its wake a major disruption to all areas of life. People reported suffering significant emotional upheaval, disruption of existing relationships, particularly with partners.
- The emotional impact and anxieties raised by health surveillance was widely commented on. Emotional support to parents is clearly as important as advice given.

**Teenagers, mental health and health promotion**
The process of 'distancing' between parents and teenagers brought with it a series of stresses for both parties.



STAFFORDSHIRE
UNIVERSITY
LIBRARY

### *Implications for health promotion*

- The pejorative connotation of the word 'mental' may signal that another prefix such as 'psychological' or 'emotional' might be used to facilitate more open discussion.
- Respondents see a strong link between poor mental health and social conditions:
  (a) Social policy striving to decrease mental ill health should look to poverty reduction and interventions which support and empower the most vulnerable.
  (b) If ordinary people attribute their difficulties to a combination of social conditions (cause) and personal responsibility (solution) then medical intervention
  may only suit some people some of the time by removing personal responsibility.
- Privacy and autonomy are often as important to people as the need to talk.
- Sport was seen by men as a stress-reducing activity, its positive impact on mental health should be given greater prominence.
- Exhortations to share difficulties may not always be well received, whereas practical tips or positively recognising efforts to cope alone might be more acceptable.
- Written information may be an important source of emotional support independent of professional contact.
- Seeking help from others who have experienced problems of their own may be appealing for those who do want help. This implies that models such as co-counselling and self-help groups might be acceptable to people who lack these opportunities in their immediate social network.
- Recognition needs to be given to lay views about what keeps people emotionally healthy, including those that may clash with physical health promotion strategies such as promotion of healthy lifestyles.

#### Antenatal care

- Antenatal classes should try and give more of a sense of the experience of having a new-born baby. Also the 'shock' and disruption to existing intimate relationships (particularly with live-in partners) needs to be given greater emphasis in antenatal information and education.
- The negative emotional impact of health surveillance during pregnancy needs to be acknowledged by healthcare workers. Mass screening may not be cost-effective health promotion intervention if it generates anxiety in those women who are likely to produce healthy babies.
- The value of emotional support from health visitors after the birth of a child should not be underestimated. However, parents need to feel supported not scrutinised.
- Information is useful and wanted – but the way that it is delivered is very important for the self-esteem of parents. Professionals giving advice should take into account the way it is likely to be received.

#### Dealing with teenagers

- Adults, parents, teachers and health professionals need to recognise particular sensitivities in negotiating trust with teenagers. Confidentiality may matter more than the intimacy of the relationship. Particular attention needs to be paid to teenagers with low self-esteem who are less likely to seek help.

- The role of friendship and support networks for teenagers should be taken into account in the planning of all interventions. An example in this regard would be to use teenagers as the main resource to prevent bullying in schools through counselling schemes.
- Given the reluctance about disclosure, any disclosure however small should be taken seriously.
- Health professionals and teachers need to be particularly aware of emotional difficulties in teenage boys and their reluctance to express personal problems.
- Discussion of parenting skills and child discipline in health promotion literature needs to take on the 'hidden' agenda of power. Discipline must not become a front for the expression of aggression.
- Information provided to teenagers regarding health topics, such as drugs, HIV/AIDS, and alcohol abuse, must take into account the anxiety which these topics provoke.

# Implications for mental health promotion – a summary

*Lay epidemiology*

The respondents' views on causes point firmly in the direction of attributing mental health problems to social conditions and family variables.

- The first implication of this is the same as from the professional discourse which puts forward the same emphases: mental health is jeopardised by a combination of direct social hardship and intervening variables, such as personality robustness and mitigating or disabling intimate relationships. In policy terms this would have implications for both poverty reduction and interventions, which support and empower impoverished and vulnerable individuals.
- A second implication is that if lay people mainly emphasise the role of environmental factors and their personal context when mental health problems arise in their lives, then they may not be receptive to bio-medical professional constructs and interventions.
- Respondents' accounts indicated that the term 'mental', whether connected to health or illness, is less acceptable to lay people than the term 'psychological'. Health promotion messages and strategies in this area may need to reflect this preference.

*Maintaining mental health*

When the responses about maintaining mental health are compared with the views held about the causes of mental health problems, it is clear that respondents have a complex attitude towards the relationship between agency (their sense of individual power) and structure (their acknowledged environmental constraints). Despite the strong consensus on *social* determinism, when coping daily or meeting sporadic emotional challenges, the respondents were obliged to develop or experiment with *individual* solutions. Broadly, these have two implications:

- Privacy and autonomy were emphasised and need to be placed alongside the ambivalent feelings respondents expressed in relation to emotional support. Such a juxtaposition suggests that simple messages like BT's 'It's good to talk', may not always find favour with ordinary people. People vary in their attitude towards coping alone and sharing their problems with others. Psychotherapists as well as telephone companies emphasise that conversation is by its very nature psychologically beneficial, but this assumption may be out of sync with the way in which most people get by in life.
- Sport is a stress-reducing activity for people. It has a direct impact on the emotional well-being of participants and a variable impact on spectators. The current emphasis on the direct physiological advantages of participation in sport within health promotion could be enlarged to recognise mental health advantages. Likewise the emotional advantages of the spectator role could be

investigated in more depth by further research. For men, the shifts over time between participating in and watching sport seemed to be closely bound up with their life stories and so might have particularly strong links with self-image and identity. Existing research suggests that in the absence of clear 'given' physical markers men may sensitise themselves to the relationship between their biography and their well-being through other means such as activity or the lack of it. This implies the need for more systematic research into gender differences in relation to sport and mental health.

### *Privacy and disclosure*

- Exhortations to share difficulties may not always be well received, whereas practical tips on coping alone might be more acceptable.
- Written information may be an important source of emotional support independent of professional contact.
- Seeking help from others who have experienced problems of their own may be appealing for those who do want help. This implies that models such as co-counselling and self-help groups might be acceptable to people who lack these opportunities in their immediate social network.
- Recognition needs to be given to lay views about what keeps people emotionally healthy, including those that may clash with physical health promotion strategies such as promoting healthy lifestyles.
- The preference for resolving issues by oneself is mirrored and reinforced by the attitudes of health professionals to their clients and health promotion literature, which emphasises individual action and responsibility. This has sometimes been criticised for adopting a victim-blaming approach. An emphasis on individualism may be functional for most people most of the time and has the added advantage of fitting in with cultural norms which have proliferated in recent times. However, this may present problems for people who will not or cannot deal with problems on their own. If seeking help is seen as deviant and a weakness, it may reinforce personal distress.

### *Professionals and emotional support*

- The availability of professionals does not necessarily translate into client confidence in their provision of support. Because primary care professionals have the highest contact level with the general population this does not mean that service users experience them as sources of support.
- Despite the common assumption that the effectiveness of GPs would be more effective if their psychiatric knowledge were increased and more emotional morbidity identified, from a service user's point of view their ordinary human qualities and practical help may be more important. Social not medical support is indicated.

### *Family relationships*

- The current division of domestic labour between men and women and between adults and their teenage children suggests that parents, particularly mothers, are carrying the responsibility for household chores. Given the psychological investment parents have in maintaining the *status quo* (because of acculturated identity) and the pay offs enjoyed by their children, it may be that the family itself is not the best target for education in this regard. It could be that expectations generated by the school curriculum about gendered household work and later role responsibilities as parents are more salient.

### *Birth, babies and toddlers*

#### Maternity care

- The psychological impact and relational issues surrounding birth and having young children might usefully be emphasised more in ante-natal education and health promotion strategies.
- Antenatal classes should try and give more of a sense of the *experience* of having a new-born baby. Bathing and other advice may be better coming from women who have just had a baby. This might inspire confidence in women about to give birth and give women who have just had a baby a sense of worth and self-confidence.
- The negative emotional impact of health surveillance during pregnancy needs to be acknowledged by healthcare workers. It should also be considered whether better targeting of techniques for those at risk during pregnancy might reduce the need for surveillance in all expectant mothers. Mass screening may not be a cost-effective health promotion intervention if it generates lasting iatrogenic anxiety in those women who are likely to produce healthy babies.
- Information is useful and wanted – but the way that it is delivered is very important for the self-esteem of parents. When giving advice professionals should take into account the way it is likely to be received. At times the need of parents to feel supported may take precedence over compliance with the content of advice. Advice about postnatal issues may not be well used antenatally. Thus, the timing and manner of information transfer is as important as its content.

#### Health visiting

- Parenting skills are seen as central to professionals' views of what parents should be doing for their children. Recent research suggests that these professional notions centre on issues to do with development – emphasising stimulation, loving environments, etc. Parental needs were rarely recognised by professionals. Health professionals' views are also likely to screen out those structural issues which, although recognised as important, are out of their control. Consequently, such issues as poverty (the key social determinants of mental health attributed by respondents) are largely absent from their interactions with parents. Alternatively they are ameliorative 'fringe' activities. The views about causes of mental healthiness examined in other parts of this report suggest that from a parental viewpoint, structural questions of finance, employment and environment are salient or overriding issues in relation to mental health and well-being. Thus a mismatch between professional and lay discourses may not make communication easy. Ignoring these factors in communications between parents and health professionals suggests that the ground rules for effective communication and understanding may from the outset be jeopardised.
- The model of working used by antenatal health workers would seem to be important in providing *appropriate* emotional and social support for families with young children. The 'care' and support element, which was a starting point for professional principles and practice of antenatal care, has gradually been transformed over a thirty-year period to a point where it has taken on the 'character of a technological surveillance programme'. There is some indication

that different models (which are more fully discussed in the main report), which focus on providing social and emotional support to mothers are more acceptable and effective. An implication of this for health visitors is that the traditional surveillance emphasis is not compatible with one which focuses on the experienced and expressed needs of parents and a brokerage model in which the health visitor mobilises aspects of the immediate social context in the interests of vulnerable individuals.

**Discipline**

The accounts about discipline have a number of implications for mental health. Parents believe that their discipline policy can affect the stability of their children by positively socialising them into acceptable habits. Additionally, some parents consider that physical punishment is unhealthy for their child's well-being and psychological development. Also, the strain of deciding how to discipline children is itself a stressor.

- Discussion of parenting skills and child discipline in health promotion literature needs to take on the 'hidden' agenda of power, and parents need to be made more aware that psychological issues to do with power and emotions might shape or underlie attitudes to discipline. Parental views about discipline may appear to be rationales about child-rearing but they may be rationalisations to protect parental power over their children and/or justifications for the expression of aggression in the family. Given that the dilemmas about discipline recur for all parents, the question of support and discussion (rather than education) returns.

*Teenagers*

- Given the importance attributed by teenagers to their peers compared to adults, parents, teachers and health professionals need to recognise particular sensitivities about negotiating trust and openness with teenage children. From our study, fostering an atmosphere of adolescent centredness would mean health professionals acknowledging that there is a preference for non-disclosure and self-reliance as coping mechanisms and for disclosing to peers amongst teenage girls. If confidence is to be inspired about the ability to deal with more serious problems such as bullying, pregnancy or risk-taking behaviour, teachers and health professionals need to listen when they are approached for help with apparently trivial problems. Our study also indicated the need for informal networks to give support to teenagers during periods of emotional upheaval. The use of peers would be useful here, for example, school-based co-counselling using pupils. Examples in this regard would be to see teenagers themselves as being the main resource to reduce bullying in schools through co-counselling schemes.
- Health professionals and health promoters need to be particularly aware of the emotional difficulties of teenage boys and the poor chance of them expressing openly personal problems. Informal networks are important to some extent in alleviating these problems, but evidence in this study suggests that boys may find less emotional support than girls. Teachers and health promoters need to be aware of the difficulties teenage boys have in expressing their feelings. Rather than relying on spontaneous disclosure of problems a more pro-active stance towards emotional support for teenage boys may be needed in school and health promotion literature which acknowledges the problems that young men of this age are likely to face and the sources of help they can turn to.
- Health promotion about a number of health topics mentioned that caused



STAFFORDSHIRE
UNIVERSITY
LIBRARY

anxiety for both parents and their teenage children, such as drug misuse and AIDS, can be seen to have a wider *mental* health implication. Information and discussion about these topics need to take into account their emotional connotations.

### *Social background differences*

If the stereotypical views of single parents found in this research are evident in the wider population then the key problem lone-parent families are likely to face in relation to mental health is the stigma attached to them from other groups who predominantly view their social status in problematic and negative terms. In this regard mental health promoters might do well to reflect the variegated and ordinary way in which single parents view themselves.

# 1. Introduction

The emphasis within *The Health of the Nation* on mental ill health suggests that health promotion research might fruitfully investigate psychological well-being. Mental health has received relatively little research attention compared to physical ill health. The illness rather than health focus within *The Health of the Nation* itself reflects a medical emphasis on pathology rather than a wider discussion of health (Department of Health, 1992). The same is true of prominent texts on preventing mental illness (Newton, 1992). This emphasis on illness rather than health is also apparent when the various frameworks used by 'mental health' professionals are compared (such as psychoanalysis, biological psychiatry, behaviourism, existentialism and humanistic psychology). Even though these theoretical approaches differ widely in their assumptions about causality, with the exception of the last in the list, their interest converges on explaining and responding to mental *illness*. Their shared interest is in aetiology and treatment. This same illness focus is true also of two major sociological traditions: labelling theory (e.g. Scheff, 1966) and social causationism (e.g. Brown and Harris, 1978). Despite the legitimate knowledge claims put forward by these research traditions in psychiatry, psychology and sociology, by emphasising illness they have pre-emptively construed the topic of *mental health*.

The focus on a professionally defined agenda about mental illness has also been at the expense of exploring empirically-based lay understandings of the relevant domestic and social contexts in which mental health is constructed, established and interpreted. Recent social research on conceptions of lay notions of health have also tended to centre on physical as opposed to psychological well-being. Mental health has not been separated out for analysis and it has tended to be subsumed under a non-health heading such as 'quality of life'. Whilst the existing work on lay conceptualisations of health draws attention to the holistic manner in which lay people view health and well-being generally, in our view examining the mental health pole of this holism is worthy of more in-depth scrutiny.

The little research which has been conducted on lay views of mental health has tended to focus on pre-defined mental illness categories (for example, the work on public perceptions of the relationship between violence and schizophrenia (Field Institute, 1984)). There is a small amount of anthropological and social research which has set out to avoid the use of illness categories in exploring people's views about mental health (e.g. Horwitz, 1983). A more recent example is a survey conducted by two of the present authors (Rogers *et al.*, 1993). However, this research was carried out on a psychiatric population (those who had been admitted to hospital at least once in the past) and again focused on mental distress rather than well-being. None the less, the research findings do suggest an agenda for the exploration of mental well-being amongst a non-psychiatric population. For example, the complexity of the views provided by patient-respondents about the nature of mental health problems contrasted starkly with the narrower constructions imposed by psychiatric and other professional discourses. Respondents identified the cause of their problems in mainly social and existential terms.

The present study extends the methodology used by recent research into lay and familial constructions of health (e.g. Backett, 1992; Davison *et al.*, 1991; Pill and

Stott, 1982; Roberts *et al.*, 1993) as a means of investigating familial conceptions of mental health as part of the make-up of everyday life. In carrying out this study we have gone beyond documenting 'lay beliefs' of pre-defined health-related behaviours. Instead, our aim has been to build up a picture of how decisions and behaviour relevant to mental health are enacted and prioritised within the fabric of family and domestic life. In other words, we have sought not only to understand family members' views about promoting mental health but to understand how these emerge and are expressed in families situated in particular social contexts. The data thus go some way to illuminate the influences and constraints of those contexts, as well as the thoughts and behaviour of the individuals studied.

## THE STUDY

In this study, whilst the use of pre-defined mental health categories has been avoided, the salience of mental health has been explored in relation to key familial events and phases, for example, pregnancy, birth and early childhood, adolescence, changes in employment situations, divorce and bereavement. Similarly, other key social variables and their relationship to conceptions of mental health have been explored (for example, gender), as well as the role of immediate social networks and other influences which have an impact on lay understandings, activities and behaviour. We have also tried to shed some light on the role that different members of the family have played in promoting and discussing issues related to mental health.

Different sections of the population are better placed than others to maintain or promote positive mental health. For example, married men gain more in terms of psychological well-being from marriage than women, and high income families are less likely to suffer from most types of mental health problems than working-class families (Brown and Harris, 1978; Hollingshead and Redlich, 1958). Thus the focus has been on different types of family and domestic units. The purpose of this has been to explore a range of understandings and contexts relevant to the promotion of positive mental health.

### *Aims*

The overall aims of the study were:

- To examine lay epidemiology and constructs in relation to mental health and well-being.
- To examine lay views about emotional support, that is, how do people define it and where do people get it from?
- To examine to what extent material differences facilitate different patterns of emotional support and use of informal and formal resources.
- To draw out from the data implications for possible mental health promotion strategies.

### *Method*

This was a qualitative study which used in-depth interviews carried out over a twelve-month period. When approaching any health topic which has previously been relatively ignored by researchers, it is particularly important to deploy a methodology which will ask open-ended questions of respondents and which allows the latter to articulate and expand upon their everyday assumptions. Thus, the chosen method used was inductive rather than hypothetico-deductive in keeping with 'grounded' theorising.

The rules of adequacy of sampling applied to qualitative research are different from those applied to quantitative methods. In this study the aim was to understand intra- and inter-familial differences, and this required the recruitment of a variety of families. In order to gain a spread of family types, both working-class and middle-class parents were interviewed, as were single parents. The former were identified according to financial, educational and occupational background. Those domestic units where an immediate family member has experienced chronic mental health problems (as indicated by admission to a psychiatric hospital or unit) were excluded from the sample. In the original proposal it was intended to include interviews with black families. However, attempts to access such families have proved difficult, with all but two families refusing to be interviewed. Attempts to use a black researcher, with knowledge of local black families in Liverpool, failed to elicit any positive responses from families to be interviewed. Two Asian families at first agreed to be interviewed and an interviewer fluent in the relevant language was recruited to carry out the interviews. However, the families later declined to be interviewed. Such difficulties have been noted by other minority ethnic groups in relation to projects about health, emotional and social support. It is clear from our experience that extensive preparatory work would be necessary to conduct this type of research with black and minority ethnic families and that separate and not insignificant funding is required to tap the views of these groups.

Two key stages in family life when mental health was likely to have been a prominent issue were taken into consideration in the choice of the proposed sample. These related to families with pre-school children and adolescents. Parents, and where relevant, teenage children, were interviewed separately in relation to the topics described below. In addition to the in-depth interviews, standard pre-coded data were collected on all families in relation to family composition, ethnicity, parental occupation, income and education.

### *The sample*

The study was carried out with families in urban and semi-rural areas of the Northwest of England. Families were recruited from Preston, Liverpool, semi-rural parts of Lancashire and the Inner and Greater Manchester areas. Part of the reason for extending the area from which families were recruited was that we felt particular parochial factors were operating in the sample from Liverpool. Families recruited from Liverpool early in the study expressed views about family closeness which we felt may not have been reproduced in other urban families in the Northwest of England. We recruited families that fitted in with a definition of class which relied on a number of social markers. Thus those families who were owner occupiers, where there was evidence of professional or graduate education and their net income was over £25,000 a year were consider to be middle class. Interviewees were also asked to comment on their own attributed class position. More will be said about the sample in the data outline below.

In each interview, interviewers followed a 'topic guide' which ensured that the respondent's views on each issue being examined in our study was discussed. This interview schedule covered the following areas:

- family responsibilities and domestic relationships;
- conceptions of physical health and well-being in the family;
- conceptions, images of the nature and causes of mental health and well-being;

- family mental health; pregnancy, birth and children under 5 and/or issues surrounding teenage mental health (e.g. education, risk-taking behaviours);
- strategies for maintaining mental health and eliciting emotional support.

Interviews lasted between 45 minutes and $2\frac{1}{2}$ hours and were taped. The interviews with teenagers tended to be shorter than with adults, and amongst the adult and teenager groups interviews were shorter with male than with female respondents. Respondents were also asked to fill in a personal details questionnaire in order to ascertain the socio-demographic features of the population under study. The questionnaire asked respondents to place themselves into categories in relation to their sex, age, accommodation, area, family size, employment position, occupation, salary, education, class, ethnicity and family position. The majority of respondents did return these questionnaires to their interviewer, although a handful of respondents did not complete their questionnaires.

### *Data analysis*

The interviews were tape-recorded, fully transcribed and analysed using the ETHNOGRAPH computer package, which is designed to facilitate the thematic analysis of qualitative data. Themes were identified at the interviewing stage and through retrospective analysis of the interviews. All the interviews carried out were transcribed, manually coded and then entered on to the ETHNOGRAPH. This means that an extremely complex dataset was produced. A coding scheme for the ETHNOGRAPH was devised and revised. The final coding schema contained 79 categories which were applied to the data and is included as Appendix C. The ETHNOGRAPH was extremely useful in producing inter- and intra-group analysis of themes.

### *The families*

A comprehensive picture of the socio-demographic background of the respondents is presented in Appendix A. Altogether 45 families were included in the study. Within these families, interviews were undertaken with 101 individuals, with seven respondents declining to be interviewed (four male partners and three teenagers). The family types of the respondents were categorised according to: working- or middle-class; parental status – two-parent or single-parent; and the age of their children – under 5 years old or teenage (see table).

Of the families with teenagers the majority (16) had one teenage child whilst 10 had two or more. Thirteen of the families were recruited from rural or semi-rural areas with the remainder living in urban areas.

| **Family type** | Number of families (children under 5) | Number of families (teenage children) |
|---|---|---|
| Working class (2-parents) | 11 (33) | 7 (13) |
| Middle class (2-parents) | 7 (12) | 9 (12) |
| Lone parent | 8 (11) | 3 (3) |
| **Total** | 26 (56) | 19 (28) |

*Numbers in brackets represent no. of individuals interviewed

### *Income and employment status*

In the category of working-class families with children under 5, five individuals classed themselves as unemployed. Family incomes ranged from £6000 to £17,000. Of the middle-class families with children under 5, three respondents classed themselves as unemployed (all of them mothers). The family incomes of this category of respondents ranged from £22,000 to £40,000. The majority of the working-class parents with teenagers were in employment, with only one father being unemployed. Family incomes in this category ranged from £11,000 to £30,000. Of the middle-class families with teenagers, all of the parents were in employment, with four mothers working part-time. Family incomes in this category ranged from £25,000 to £40,000. Of the three single mothers with children under 5, two were unemployed and on benefits, with the other earning £8500. Of the single-parent families with teenagers, one single mother was in receipt of a student grant. Of the others, salaries ranged from £12,000 to £17,000.

### *The teenage group*

Of the twenty-eight teenagers interviewed, all were in full-time education. Twenty-five were at secondary school, and three in Further Education college. The majority of those interviewed (17) were aged between 15 and 16, a further eleven were aged 12–14 and three were aged between 17 and 19.

Throughout the report names are either avoided or first names used are pseudonyms, in order to protect the identity of the respondents.

### *Putting the data in context*

The main chapters of the report summarise the findings from the interviews. Before moving on to a discussion of these findings, it is important to emphasise two contextual points. First, whilst it is custom and practice in research reports to situate any study within an existing relevant literature at the outset, in this study the section headings represent quite diverse areas which have already accrued varying amounts of research scrutiny. Consequently, we have broken with tradition in order to provide a more coherent account by discussing the data in relation to other work chapter by chapter, rather than provide a literature review here at the beginning.

Secondly, an overriding consideration about the interview material discussed is its veracity and depth. Even before starting the data collection we were aware that we were attempting to elicit views and experiences which might be both difficult and even emotive because mental health is an inherently personal issue. For this reason, before leaving this outline of the study we provide an overview about the issue of private and public accounts and illustrate it in relation to the present study and its data.

## PRIVATE AND PUBLIC ACCOUNTS

A recurring aspect of the data was a split between private and public accounts. Cornwell (1984) in her research on working-class people's accounts of health and illness found that public accounts tended to be given early on in interviews in relation to questions about familial relationships and where sensitive issues or criticisms were likely. Public accounts are safe, uncritical and inoffensive. Not all research on sensitive issues has the same division between public and private accounts. The research we conducted on users' views of psychiatric services (Rogers *et al.*, 1993) were seemingly devoid of public accounts – there appeared to be no necessity to hide criticisms of professionals or treatment or to evade emotional issues. Clearly undergoing the vagaries of becoming a psychiatric patient removes shyness or reticence about these issues.

The same cannot be said of the current research, which is using a non-clinical set of respondents. There was a clear demarcation between private and public accounts. Much of the interviewers' time was spent trying to get beyond the public accounts of what people said. This difficulty also led the researchers to consider the notions of privacy and its relationship to the expression of emotional issues. A question was introduced on what people felt about the public disclosure of personal life in order to understand the cultural meaning of privacy. Respondents pointed to the acceptability of expressing personal issues as they relate directly to a political issue – such as changing the law on divorce or rape – or if the point is humorous, i.e. intended to make people laugh, as in the Esther Rantzen show. Personal disclosure for its own sake and the expression of distress, however, was often viewed as exhibitionistic and unwarranted and the motives of people who do this were subjected to questioning. Current dominant (British) cultural mores about privacy may also be implicated in our respondents' level of ability and willingness to articulate definitions of mental health when directly questioned. Typically they gave good definitions of physical health; poor definitions of mental health and good definitions of mental illness. This is illustrated by the following account – not just the content but the *ease* with which people talk about physical health and *unease* when talking about mental health:

INTERVIEWER: How would you describe your family's health generally?
RESPONDENT: Good.
INTERVIEWER: What sort of thing do you do to keep healthy?
RESPONDENT: Swimming, I haven't always got time, but he plays golf when he can really, there's not an awful lot really, he started to go to the gym the other week . . . I'm conscious of diet, I've been on a Slimming World diet and I've been on all kinds of diets and I don't eat an awful lot, you know yourself by the time you've made everyone meals, and . . . no one will eat the same thing, it's always different. You end up cooking them four different meals, so by the time you've done all that you can't be bothered cooking or sitting down for yourself.
INTERVIEWER: If I said 'mental health' what does that term mean to you, what kind of things does it suggest?
RESPONDENT: I don't know really . . . mental health?
INTERVIEWER: OK, what about psychological health, does that mean anything to you?
RESPONDENT: No.
INTERVIWER: OK, what about emotions, what do they mean to you?
RESPONDENT: How do you mean?
INTERVIWER: If somebody said to you, define what emotions are, from your own understanding and experience could you explain what it means to you?
RESPONDENT: We all have a whinge, don't we really? You know what I mean, I think it does you good.

However, it is important to note that the professional discourse about mental health is highly contested which suggests that there are genuine conceptual difficulties in this area which tax lay people and experts alike (see Appendix B).

Surface and public accounts and deep and private accounts of emotional issues co-exist within the discursive potential of ordinary people. Put simply, it would seem that immediate and unexplored responses only gave a partial representation of the inner life of our respondents about mental health. This raises a methodological problem about the credibility of personal accounts, which are the mainstay of much qualitative research in social science. If our interpretations about the hidden and private aspects of emotional life are valid, this may have implications for other studies, with health promotion implications which are vulnerable to such partiality. The question of latent meaning is complicated further by the contradictory statements which emerged within the narratives of respondents. People gave contradictory accounts which, none the less, made some sense when their dilemmas about their identity or relationship to significant others were placed into a family context. With these contradictions in mind we now move to the findings of the study.

# 2. Lay epidemiology

In this section we address the issue of how lay people understand what mental health is and what causes they attribute to mental ill health.

## DEFINITIONS OF MENTAL HEALTH

Previous research on lay views of health suggests that some areas are deemed more worthy of comment by lay respondents than others. For example, Pill and Stott (1982) noted the hesitance of respondents when discussing aetiological matters. This appears to be linked to what people perceive to be the legitimate boundaries of lay and professional knowledge. Lay people are used to being asked what they feel about things and to articulate symptoms by professionals working in health services. However, they are less frequently asked about what they view to be the *causes* of illness because of the expectation that this is the province of experts rather than lay people. This expectation was candidly put by this working-class male respondent:

INTERVIEWER: We're trying to find out what keeps people mentally healthy.
RESPONDENT: I don't know. I can't answer that one. You need a psychologist for that ... Who's to know what goes on in people's minds? Why do some people suddenly flip their lids? I don't know. If I could answer that one I wouldn't be sat here with you!

Respondents often found difficulties in finding appropriate terminology or in expressing what they considered was inexpressible (see below). However, although they struggled with the task, they did consider that, in principle, what caused mental healthiness or ill health was their legitimate province.

We explored lay views about mental health and illness in a number of ways. In the light of the pilot interviews sensitising us to the possible difficulties with lay definitions of mental health, an opening gambit was to ask respondents about their views of physical health. Then we asked what the term 'mental health' meant to them. In order to undertake a more in-depth exploration, we asked them about images of mental healthiness.

## PHYSICAL HEALTH AND MENTAL HEALTH

Recent work in the area of lay health knowledge has demonstrated that what is construed to be healthiness and the way it is assessed are problematic and contested. Relative to physical health, mental healthiness is even less tangible or easy to construe. From childhood, people develop an increasing familiarity with their bodies through their senses. Our physicality gives a direct sense of knowing about physical health and deviations from norms of physical well-being are given by both outward signs and subjective symptoms. Hence there are common reports like, 'I'm not feeling myself today' or 'I think I'm getting a cold'. By contrast, reflectiveness about one's own behaviour and inner mental states is less well developed. Indeed, some theories, like the depth psychologies, have it that we have to remain ignorant of most of our psychological states most of the time in order to survive, function and preserve a positive sense of self.

Lay definitions of physical health do include an emotional element. The holistic ways in which people view health have been noted by a number of previous studies (e.g. Backett, 1987). However, whilst people may episodically recognise mental healthiness and physical healthiness as being interconnected, the lay discourse more readily focuses on the more tangible and familiar aspects of physical health. For example, parents can talk readily about the behavioural impact of food on the healthiness of their children. Similarly, stress at work is seen to cause psychosomatic illness, so the reference point is still untoward physical outcomes like hypertension and ulcers. Perhaps one of the reasons for this better articulation about physical illness relates to the extent to which people perceive that they have control over physical-health-maintaining activities as opposed to mental health ones. As one respondent noted:

> I don't think I think of it [mental health] the same as physical health really. You can't control things as you can with getting cancer . . . like getting food and getting their sleep and keeping them safe. Whereas mental health is more difficult.

For some respondents, situating mental health in the body was the only reference point of understanding. In response to the question 'What does the term mental health mean to you?' responses included: 'Something to do with the brain' and 'That's what's in your head, isn't it really.' This construction is not merely a feature of lay ignorance, given that a part of the professional discourse about mental health and illness focuses singularly on assumed bodily determinants of behaviour (examples of this include biological psychology, organic psychiatry and socio-biology).

Unlike physical health, which is often the focus of people's everyday lives, mental health remains in the background, unacknowledged and, as this respondent notes, only makes its presence felt when things go wrong:

> It's a very difficult thing to explain [mental health], because you don't go around thinking about it, most of the time . . . things are just chugging along really. Then it can strike you out of the blue. Suddenly you realise you are not coping, and its different from being ill physically because somehow you are aware you are not feeling too good. I mean with both [physical and mental health] you've got ill and not ill but most of the time with physical health you're somewhere in between. But with mental health you're just not aware what's going on until it's too late.

'Balanced', 'emotionally controlled', 'stable' or 'coping' were other words used to describe mental well-being and were much more common than phrases such as 'the way one feels' or 'being happy'. Although both men and women used expressions which implied the ability to cope or control things in everyday life, women were more likely to make reference to feelings, for example, what they were 'feeling like inside' and men to identify themes of stability, control and rationality. As this man put it:

> I think it means keeping in touch with reality and your place in it. Not deluding yourself either about your own capabilities or the world or situations around you . . . Level-headedness. Keeping your feet firmly on the floor.

Usually this was seen as being an individual characteristic, as the quote above indicates. The most clear expression of this was the response given by a man after being asked if he could think of somebody who was psychologically unhealthy. He identified Edwina Currie, 'because she can't control what she says'.

At other times, the preconditions of maintaining stability and coping were seen to extend beyond the individual. This was most notable in relation to the female respondents as indicated by these two responses:

> Mental health means being able to cope with situations that life throws up at you. And that's not always easy when you haven't got anyone else that you can turn to for help on a regular basis.
>
> It means how well you deal with life.

Similarly, the ability to make contact with others was viewed as an aspect of mental health more often by women than men:

INTERVIEWER: What does the term psychological well-being suggest to you?
RESPONDENT: Well, cliché, happiness – but you're not happy all the time, obviously you're going to be depressed sometimes. I mean I would say communicating, because the most important thing to me is communication in the community as well as the family. I think that's why I worry about my son because he doesn't talk to enough people.

These gendered notions may shed light on the interpretation by some social scientists that men do not readily use their emotions as a resource in the public and private sphere (Hochschild, 1983). What our data does imply is that to do so overtly may for men imply weakness and loss of control.

Intelligence was also at times seen as a sign of mental health – this was particularly a theme amongst *teenagers*. This is perhaps not surprising when seen in the context of the value that teenagers place on education, school life and academic success (see Chapter 7, 'Teenagers, mental health and health promotion'). A teenage respondent comments here:

INTERVIEWER: How would you describe a mentally healthy person?
RESPONDENT: Intelligent. It's not just the stage in their school work or anything, it's what they know about the world in general. Like common sense. Wisdom is more than getting A levels or whatever. Everyone has to know common sense and the more you know the more you get on in the world.

This emerging conflation of intelligence and mental health in schoolchildren may underpin the common confusion many adults later feel between mental health problems and learning disability.

## MENTAL HEALTH OR MENTAL ILLNESS?

Where more definitive answers were given about the notion of mental health they tended to focus immediately on mental ill health and/or learning difficulties, ('backward', 'slow', 'retarded'). Sometimes this referred directly to medical categories, such as 'depression' and 'schizophrenia'. People mentioned institutions and invoked images of the neglected care-in-the-community patient. Some saw these people as separate, essentially as 'other', whilst some made connections with themselves. One respondent, for example, juxtaposed mental health and illness.

Images of mental health for this women was described as 'happy families running through the woods'. She then spontaneously went on to talk about mental illness:

> I don't tend to class depression and things like that as mental illness. Mentally ill to me has always conjured up the visions of the slightly deranged, the particular characters that wander round town centres rather than people in their homes getting on with their daily life and perhaps needing tranquillisers and anti-depressants or that kind of thing.

The above response is consistent with the study by Jones and Cochrane (1981), which found that lay people stereotype mental illness as florid psychosis and do not mention depression, which is the commonest diagnosis given by professionals. Others were more willing to see mental health and illness as more of a continuum to which they themselves were susceptible:

> Well – mental health – I suppose I see images of institutions and dark minds, people in the streets who do strange things that aren't conventional or normal. Having said that I can see how mental health can be jeopardised by things going on in your life. Sometimes I feel like I'm walking on a tightrope and it would be easy for something to tip me off balance.

A similar ambivalence was expressed by this respondent but in relation to the notion of 'stress'. As with the professional discourse this seems to indicate both an external force (a stressor) and an internal state (feeling stressed), as well as the latter being both a symptom of distress and a motivation for action:

> ... [stress] is what people think it is. Basically if you have got to say that something is stressful, it's not good, it's become something negative. You've got stress from being overloaded but then again you've got stress from being bored as well. It's just a different type of stress. Stress can also be good for you. It can make you motivated, get things done.

'Stress' was used liberally in respondents' accounts. All respondents referred to it in discussing everyday interactions and events and to refer to untoward and unexpected aspects of life. In this it mirrored the wide use of the term in the psychological and health literatures. Because the term stress referred to such a wide range of aspects of people's lives it lacked a specificity to mental health *per se*. Certainly people expected an amount of stress in their lives and it was not viewed as an aetiological factor in the same way, for example, that life events were.

The use of the term 'mental health' contrasted starkly with respondents' use of the word 'stress'. What was clear from the accounts was that the term 'mental', whether followed by the word 'health' or 'illness' was regarded in negative and fearful terms. As one respondent expressed it, 'I suppose just the word "mental" in itself, just a single word is rather derogatory to a layman. It's intimidating really.' These notions were generally attributable to media images of mental illness and more recently of community care. Familial attitudes were also mentioned.

MALE RESPONDENT: I grew up in a family that was not unemotional but not really receptive to strange people.

INTERVIEWER: Strange people?

MALE RESPONDENT: Strange in inverted commas, people who were different to what they [parents] are.

INTERVIEWER: And what effect do you think that had on you?



STAFFORDSHIRE UNIVERSITY LIBRARY

MALE RESPONDENT: I grew up that way. Intolerant – not receptive to people different to yourself.

A more acceptable way of discussing and promoting mental health may be by replacing the term 'mental health' with 'psychological' or 'emotional health', which were deemed to be less stigmatising by some respondents:

RESPONDENT: The word 'mental' – it immediately comes to my mind about mental illness, so that's a pre-conceived idea in association with 'mental' and 'mental home'.
INTERVIEWER: So what other term could you use for things that didn't cover physical things?
RESPONDENT: Perhaps *psychological* health. If you said to me 'what about psychological health?', I would think what you think about health as being healthy – to do with your mind as opposed to mental, as soon as you say 'mental' to me that just conjures up mental homes...

There were indications that the term 'psychological' is more acceptable than the term 'mental' because of its association with a prestigious academic subject. A number of respondents indicated an exposure to psychological knowledge. Leaving aside the one or two respondents who were actually studying psychology as a topic part-time, others mentioned relatives or children studying it at A level or they themselves had been exposed to some psychological ideas during training. This was not confined to those involved in 'caring' professions, such as probation or nursing, but extended to those who had worked in commercial environments, where psychological processes were associated with advertising products.

## CAUSES OF MENTAL HEALTH PROBLEMS

The various theories put forward by our respondents about the causation of mental healthiness and unhealthiness mirrored the discourses of mental health professions and academic disciplines. As will be seen from the accounts given by our respondents below, these ranged from the biological to the psychological through to the sociological. There was also a variety of ways in which respondents *expressed* these theories which involved a combination of medical and psychological terms and understanding, combined with a lay view. Here is an example of how lay and psychiatric terminology coalesce:

> You need to be well, if you've got a broken leg, that can cause you a bit of mental anguish, if you can't get out and do things. You can have something that makes you depressed, like a reactive depression, like I am about this court case last week. But when you don't get over that reaction you become clinically depressed. It's when you get something that upsets you you've got to get over it, then if you don't you just go into a quagmire of worrying about yourself, and it becomes like an illness rather than just a reaction to something that's happened to you.

Not all potential causes were given the same weight. A preference for life events, family problems and economic hardship was mentioned frequently but genetic causes were noted much less often – and usually as an addendum to these other cited causes.

## GENDERED NOTIONS OF MENTAL HEALTH AND ILLNESS

A number of studies have pointed to the gendered notions of mental health and illness used by professionals (Broverman *et al.*, 1970; Fabrikant, 1974). There has also been some research which indicates that these notions may be prevalent amongst lay people, as well as mental health professionals. Jones and Cochrane (1981) found from responses to a series of scales made up of terms depicting opposite personal characteristics (for example, 'outgoing versus withdrawn', 'sensitive versus insensitive') that respondents clearly differentiated in the adjectives they chose to describe the differences between mentally unhealthy men and women. In contrast, the terms used to describe normal women and mentally ill women were similar. Gendered notions of the causes and nature of mental health were prevalent in the study reported here. Here a female respondent depicts this in the context of the breakdown of the institution of marriage:

> A lot of depression today is women on their own bringing their children up, and menopausal women whose husbands have left them.

The respondent then went on to express the point of view that even though her mother had an unhappy marriage, this was better than having to suffer the indignity of being left by a husband:

> My mum in a way had a terrible marriage but we were OK mentally, it's such a knock to your self-confidence when somebody leaves you, deserts you for somebody else, it's like the feelings of rejection are so bad.

This and other accounts are clearly rooted in personal experience. This woman was divorced and was still in legal dispute with her husband about access and finances, which she reported as having a negative impact on her mental health. Expectations accompanying a dual domestic role were also viewed as a precursor to stress, leading to diminishing psychological health as indicated by these two women respondents:

> [People] trying to do too many things, and cope on their own, when they should ask for help. Coping with a job and a family, I think, can be very stressful. I think people expect more of you these days than they did at one time.
>
> ......................................................
>
> I suppose that the biggest stress in my life at one time was my mother. Simply because of the amount she expected me to do. In terms of how a home should be run. And I couldn't do it and look after Liz, and work full-time as well. It was too much. And the more I tried, the more she expected, and the harder it got.

This last quote suggests it is not merely the sheer burden of undertaking combined work in domestic and non-domestic contexts but the pressure to undertake these roles in an uncompromising manner. Such images of 'super mum' are prevalent in women's magazines and, according to some respondents, appear as well in social networks.

## LIFE EVENTS

Major life events were cited as the predominant cause of poor mental health. Events that were recurrently mentioned were divorce, bereavement, unemployment and financial difficulties. Financial difficulties, the stress of work and unemployment were the most frequently cited factors considered to affect mental well-being.

## THE IMPACT OF FINANCES AND UNEMPLOYMENT

Financial hardship was mentioned by respondents from families from all backgrounds. In the middle-class families, this tended to be in recognition of the pressures people faced from different class backgrounds to themselves. In terms of the frequency with which certain life events or long-term difficulties were mentioned, financial difficulties featured more in accounts of the working-class respondents. Adequate financial arrangements and job security were the basis of both good physical and mental health according to this respondent:

> It's all down to money. All your problems are money problems. All the problems on them pages [the interviewer's schedule] are to do with money. Money, your job and your health. That's the main three ingredients. If you've got a job and it's secure you've cracked it.

The relationship between financial hardship and mental health was frequently elaborated upon:

> Well, not having any money is a real big thing. Yes, you've got to pay your bills and it's like stressful, just thinking how you are going to pay one bill and you haven't got the money, what are you going to do? The electric's going to get cut off and you're going to get thrown out of your house. Money is the big thing.

Long-term difficulties or the build-up of events over time were identifiable from accounts – chronic unresolved money worries were frequently mentioned in this regard. Everyday stresses were also identified as leading to mental health problems:

> Everyday stress, kids, money is a big stress – bills you can't pay, car breaking down.

## LOSS

Loss in its broadest sense was also viewed as a causal factor in mental health problems. This notion was not confined to loss in terms of being bereaved but was similar to that described by Brown and Harris (1978) in their classic *Social Origins of Depression*. Here a women describes what she thinks diminishes mental health:

> The losses really. Loss of a job – loss of anything. And changes in circumstances. Kids moving away, going away to college, getting married. Once they've gone you'd do anything to have them back.

There were also the equivalent lay views about vulnerability and protective factors (see Chapter 3, 'Maintaining mental health').

Respondents also elaborated on the processes which made particular events or characteristics pathogenic. Here a young women relates the relationship between unemployment as a cause of mental health and the immediate social environment in which people live:

> I mean if you live in a sort of area where the general feeling is very much pessimistic rather than optimistic ... tends to spread. Especially in areas of high unemployment. It can't be very good for anyone.

Unemployment was a prominent feature of many of the accounts, as were descriptions about lack of finances, poor urban environments and gender. Whilst (as can be seen in Chapter 8, 'Views about social background') these issues were at times viewed as relative, for example, affecting those with higher as well as lower incomes, mental health or illness was not something which was viewed as striking anyone at any time but was something that was clearly socially patterned and caused.

## THE RELATIONSHIP BETWEEN LAY AND PROFESSIONAL VIEWS OF CAUSALITY

Professional knowledge about mental health and mental health problems is highly contested, with a wide range of theories abounding which implicate bodily, personal and social variables both separately and in permutations (see Pilgrim and Rogers, 1993, chapter 1, for a summary). The medical anthropologist Nancy Scheper-Hughes has also highlighted a wider linguistic problem in contemporary Western societies, which disables professionals and lay people alike:

> We are without a language with which to address mind–body–society interactions, and so are left hanging mid-air, suspended in hyphens that testify to the radical disconnectedness of our thoughts. We resort to such fragmented concepts as the bio-social, the psychosomatic, the psycho-social, the somato-social as a feeble way of expressing the complex and myriad ways that our minds speak to us through our bodies, and the way in which society is inscribed on the expectant canvas of our flesh and bones, blood and guts.

Thus, both professionals and lay people tend to manage this absence of an integrated linguistic framework to understand body, mind and society interactions by emphasising, or even reducing a phenomenon to, one of the three components or a particular dimension within their preferred domain of explanation.

It was mentioned above that only a few respondents alluded to genetic causation and even then it was in ways that would not meet with the approval of geneticists. For example, one man thought that mental health problems were caused by the 'genes getting mixed up'. What is clear overall is that the respondents, independent of their own class background, tended to favour environmentalist explanations and that, within these, financial insecurity and poverty predominated as assumed determinants of poor mental health. We have also noted that some of the female respondents commented on the particular stresses which women experience when struggling with a dual role of motherhood and career. These notions are clearly close to that part of the professional discourse which has focused on the interaction of social class and gender in relation to mental health (e.g. Brown and Harris, 1978).

Not only were biological explanations a minority part of the discourse but so were notions of a dynamic unconscious associated with psychoanalysis and other forms of depth psychology. It would seem that the dominant lay position on causality could be described as a form of 'social determinism' within social science. And within this approach there is an emphasis upon the interaction between people as agents, coping as best they can and deploying where possible cognitive ingenuity (see Chapter 3, 'Maintaining mental health'), on the one hand, and an acknowledgement of social stressors, constraints and opportunities on the other. This dominant lay discourse about causality is not fanciful. It is consistent, for example, with the data on the over-representation of women in psychiatric statistics and with the findings of quantitative empirical investigations of the relationship between job stress, unemployment and mental health scores.

As Fryer (1995) has recently pointed out, when reviewing the literature on the relationship between job status and mental health, that unemployment has a double impact. It thwarts and baffles a person's sense of agency *and* it brings with it poverty, which is pregnant with a whole range of stressful challenges. These include debt, non-repayment of HP, power disconnections and periods when basic necessities cannot be purchased (Cooke, 1987). In addition, when newly unemployed, a person's previous range of activities become unaffordable and therefore their life becomes more restricted (Warr and Payne, 1983). Moreover, the unemployed person experiences a contrast between their previous or expected material conditions, according to their social reference group, and their actual experience. This relative deprivation means that middle-class people can also become distressed by unemployment and they can experience anticipatory anxiety about this state when in employment which is under threat. In his review of the literature on mental health and employment, Fryer (1995, p.270) makes the point that:

> Unsurprisingly, unemployed people consistently tell us – when we allow them – that their major problems revolve around money, and indicators of psychological distress are associated with measures of both subjective and objective financial distress.

This summary is consistent with the emphases given within the group of respondents we interviewed.

## IMPLICATIONS FOR MENTAL HEALTH PROMOTION

- Because of the complex reasons why lay people struggle with defining mental health, there are few pointers about securing greater consensus on the matter. As noted in this section, it is not as though experts are at one about definitions and so they have no consensus to simplify and communicate to lay people. However, the pejorative connotation of the word 'mental' may signal that another prefix such as 'psychological' or 'emotional' may encourage a greater facility for discussion about the topic.

The respondents' views on causes point firmly in the direction of attributing mental health problems to social conditions and family variables.

- The first implication of this is the same as from the professional discourse which puts forward the same emphases: mental health is jeopardised by a combination of direct social hardship and intervening variables, such as personality robustness and mitigating or disabling intimate relationships. In policy terms this would have implications for both poverty reduction and interventions, which support and empower impoverished and vulnerable individuals (Newton, 1992).
- A second implication is that if lay people mainly emphasise the role of environmental factors and their personal context when mental health problems arise in their lives, then they may not be receptive to biomedical professional

constructions and interventions. Such a disjuncture was found in a previous study by the authors (Rogers *et al.*, 1993). If ordinary people attribute their difficulties to a combination of social conditions (cause) and personal responsibility (solutions to be found – see Chapter 3) then a medical intervention may only suit some people some of the time, by removing personal responsibility. The medicalisation of psychosocial problems will be met with ambivalence from those experiencing them.

# 3. Maintaining mental health

In Chapter 2 it is noted that the dominant view about the *causes* of mental health problems is essentially one of social determinism. In this chapter it becomes clear that the struggle to *preserve* mental health emphasises individual ingenuity – agency not structure is privileged. That is, individuals generally consider that they have little immediate control over external constraints and stressors, and so they focus in their own lives on what they believe they can control – their own actions.

## SELF-RELIANCE

One method of maintaining mental health described by respondents was that of self-reliance or a striving for autonomy. This had both inner or subjective features and outward relational characteristics. The former entailed drawing consciously on reserves for coping. The latter involved using the support or positive feedback of others to boost one's own morale. Examples of these methods can be seen in the views expressed by one respondent:

> Well, it's just helping you achieve your goal really – you do need people to tell you – you just need that bit of boost from other people to say 'you're doing really well and keep on going'.

Ideally she thinks one should be doing this independently of others:

> I suppose you couldn't really keep telling yourself that, you'd need somebody else to tell you it as well . . . I don't think it helps when you start relying on certain pills to help you get by, you just have to be strong in yourself and try and get over it yourself.

Knowing one's own strengths and limitations was also central to this, as was the need 'to be yourself'. For example, here she is talking about how she resolved a period of illness and not coping well. She started to get over this:

> . . . by slowing down and not worrying about what people think. And they've got to like you for what you are and take you for what you are, and if they don't like it then that's tough. You cannot really go out of your way to prove yourself. You have just got to be yourself and do what you are capable of doing and not exceed that.

She also considered it important to find time alone:

> . . . you need to escape and just think about yourself for a few hours. . .

This notion that finding time to be alone in order to stay mentally healthy was mentioned by another respondent.

> I like to go out on my own now and again when the kids are in bed. Before I was pregnant I was working part-time and that helped a lot. I just used to enjoy just getting out.

A rigid view about autonomy is implied by this respondent, who considered that people either had to get on and cope with life's pressures on their own or enter the patient role. This suggests a neat division between self-reliance or mental illness with no middle ground:

INTERVIEWER: What do you think people do to stop that pressure building up so much that they do lose control?
RESPONDENT: See a psychiatrist?
INTERVIEWER: Anything else?
RESPONDENT: No.

By contrast, this female respondent considers that the two most important elements in maintaining mental health are:

> Communication with other people and having a good social network of people you can discuss problems with.

Indeed some of the respondents that placed an emphasis on self-reliance also pointed to the important role of other people at times for support or for helpful conversations. As an indication of the complexity of this issue of self-reliance, here we cite a young Asian woman who when feeling down would be ashamed to show it to her father and so strives to achieve what Goffman (1968) called 'passing' – she tries to make out that no problem exists:

> There's some things that make me feel down but I act happy. If someone says something bad to you or criticises you or anything, you act happy like you couldn't care . . . you say to yourself 'that's not going to get me down – just forget about it'. But there is a little bit of you somewhere that does get down . . . nobody knows that, nobody at all but you. It's just there.

Self-reliance is important. It may reflect a tradition of individualism and a concern to protect privacy or the role of shame.

## COGNITIVE STRATEGIES

Whilst self-reliance entails taking up a position about relations with others, an inner state of confidence was important for respondents when they spoke of maintaining mental health. This respondent, was middle class and had children under 5. He considered that being over-optimistic tempted a fall and that pessimism was a more realistic middle ground. However, he then goes on to say:

> . . . but I'm sure if you're optimistic you see a reason to try and make it happen . . . if you believe you can achieve a goal as opposed to just having a goal . . .

Another respondent, when asked about maintaining mental health, said:

> I think just being aware of what problems are, is having a strategy to cope with them. Sometimes it might be just not thinking about it for a short time and then



STAFFORDSHIRE UNIVERSITY LIBRARY

> going back to it. I think if you are aware of problems then you can cope with them because you can work out what the best way is [of coping or solving them]. But sometimes you are not aware that you have a problem and it takes an outsider, parents or friends to sort of say 'look ...'.

This is echoed in another respondent in these terms:

> You can only have peace of mind if you know what maybe the problem is. So if you are worried about something, if you can get to know what you are worried about, like it gives you peace of mind, stops the anxiety and stops the mental thing...

These responses suggests that for some the traditional notion of 'insight', whether arrived at alone or with the help of others, is important. To an extent this is consistent with empirical research into the relationship between process and outcome in psychological therapies. Whilst this research suggests that insight is not always necessary for sustained emotional, cognitive and behavioural change, in some settings, such as marital problem-solving and satisfaction, it is associated with the greatest improvements (Bergin and Garfield, 1994).

The last respondent also noted that if she was feeling down her first response would be to go and buy herself a box of chocolates. This suggests that for her there are immediate coping mechanisms and there are longer-term strategies about problem-solving.

Here one man explains that his view about adapting to life changes relies on a mixture of moral obligation or personal responsibility (note first phrase below) and cognitive ingenuity. On being asked how people can cope with changes he says:

> I think they have to come to terms with them, then decide how they are going to fit into the new world around them or how they are going to make their little world fit them. They can change the external factors or fit into the new environment. I don't think there's a lot of other choice really ... I think that sometimes there's a feeling that change is a big impossible process and I think it can sometimes help to break it down and tackle it a little bit at a time...

The issue of moral responsibility noted at the start of this vignette was echoed by this woman in response to the question 'what do you think you can do to keep mentally healthy?', when she alludes to her general philosophy and her depressed husband:

> You've just got to be happy and you've got to try and be with your friends or just talk about it rather than keeping it to yourself and your friends will make you feel better. But he's got no friends and he can't talk to anyone. He's just got to try and think positive rather than thinking negative all the time – which I know is hard but you've got to try ... That's the only thing you can do, otherwise you'll be just on a downer all the time...

This respondent, describes how he needs time alone to work problems out before talking to others:

> I'll either go out for a walk and think about it or sit in the garden where it's quiet and just let it go through my mind about the best way to solve the problem if I can ... I like to be organised. I think I like to know what I'm doing before I do it. I like to plan. I plan a lot, thinking about what I'm going to do and things like that ... Well, after I've thought it through, if it concerned the family I'd probably talk it through with my wife or the person involved...

Other respondents also emphasised the need to have time to reflect alone when faced with a problem in life before involving others:

> I give time to myself. Time to think it over properly. I don't ask other people their opinions straightaway to try to help me out with it. I just give myself time to mull it over. I think that I shield myself from the shock at the beginning like a numb couple of hours and then start thinking it over. I don't sort of panic straightaway or anything like that. I just sort of give myself a bit of time. I tend to have a couple of hours where I work things out for myself and then I'll go out and I've sort of made my own decisions. Then I'll talk to other people and take advice from them or whatever...

These last two respondents point to the relationship between self-reliance and the careful use of other people for help.

## SPORT AND OTHER STRESS-REDUCING ACTIVITIES

Sport is a theme which was a very important issue for men in discussing mental health. The absence of sporting outlets or disappointments about sport for some were placed on a par with other causes of mental health problems. For example, when asked what causes mental health problems this respondent made the following comment:

> Depression, a shock, death in the family, injury, financial problems or your football team not doing well ... If my team loses I am very touchy for the rest of the day...

Here another respondent, makes a similar point:

> Well I feel that I need to have something independent, something that is me and I go away whenever I do it. I'm not sort of Dave, father, breadwinner, however you want to phrase it. Sometimes I'm like Dave, the little lad down the street sort of... It's mainly football, sport or something that has been consistent throughout my life and I think I need that sort of to stabilise me.

This enthusiasm for sport was seen as important in negotiating about children's welfare. This mother has a complex view. She believes that sport is good for male children, because she considers it is good for her husband, but also worries that this view could be forced inappropriately on to her child:

> I want Jack to do lots of sports but he might not be a sporty person. Like, *you* are interested in it but he might not be. He might be interested in quiet things, intellectual things. I mean deep down you hope he will be good at sports because Mick's interested in sports, and for him, personally, he needs to do sports to keep his mind sane. He makes that connection. He feels that's an important thing. So at the moment we are looking for schools in the area and we'll make sure that they're doing sports and they've got playing fields...

Another stress-reducing activity was mentioned by this woman:

> I go to a meditation group once a week which I find quite helpful. Not from any religious point of view. I have to say, in fact, that I don't usually feel like going... I usually feel better afterwards...

Men were more likely to mention physical means of staying mentally healthy. One man linked martial arts and yoga to increasing mental capacity.

## PROTOPROFESSIONALISED RESPONSES

DeSwaan (1990) has noted that within modern Western societies some people, who are not mental health professionals themselves, develop, through their reading and contact with experts, a view which deviates from a lay perspective. This process, leading to an in-between position, DeSwaan calls 'protoprofessionalisation'. Such a process may occur to a variety of degrees according to the level of contact with experts and degree of exposure to and interest in common sources of information such as articles and agony columns in women's (and now men's) magazines (Rose, 1990; Pilgrim and Rogers, 1994).

Some respondents had been in contact with psychological experts or had experienced group or family therapy. This had left a trace in their constructions about mental health. For example, this parent of teenagers, made the following comment:

> ... people feel safe to be the people they really are within the family boundaries and sometimes they might have defences outside, especially the children, but they feel safe to express themselves within the perimeters when they're at home. Even though it can be stressful and chaotic for the family sometimes, I still think that it's preferable that they feel safe to do it at home . . . So they should do it within the family...

The notions of authenticity, defences, boundaries and contained acting out were derived from the family and marital therapy experienced by this man and informed his pre-formulated position on healthy parental permission. He moves here from talking of his children's use of the safety of the home and family to his own:

> I might go to work and put on a facade, come back and lose my temper at home, perhaps wrongly, but I can heal the wound at home and apologise for it. I don't think that it should be somewhere where you should displace all your frustrations at work, but occasionally from time to time because it has to be recognised that well from my point of view, I'm human and these things happen, but I'm accepted in the family and I'm forgiven and the wounds are healed.

As well as using terms like 'displace', the use of notions about healing again reflect a professional psychotherapeutic discourse.

## IMPLICATIONS FOR MENTAL HEALTH PROMOTION

When the responses in this chapter are compared with the views held about the causes of mental health problems discussed in Chapter 2, it is clear that respondents have a complex or sophisticated attitude towards the relationship between agency (their sense of individual power) and structure (their acknowledged environmental constraints). Despite the strong consensus on *social* determinism, when coping daily or meeting sporadic emotional challenges the respondents were obliged to develop or experiment with *individual* solutions. Broadly, these have two implications:

- Privacy and autonomy were emphasised and need to be placed alongside the ambivalent feelings respondents expressed in relation to emotional support (see Chapter 4). Such a juxtaposition suggests that simple messages like BT's 'It's good to talk', may not always find favour with ordinary people. People vary in their attitude towards coping alone and sharing their problems with others. Psychotherapists as well as telephone companies emphasise that conversation is *by its very nature* psychologically beneficial, but this assumption may be out of sync with the way in which most people get by in life.
- Sport was seen by most men in this study as a stress-reducing activity for people. It has a direct impact on the emotional well-being of participants and a variable impact on spectators. The current emphasis on the direct physiological advantages of participation in sport within health promotion could be enlarged to recognise mental health advantages. Likewise the emotional advantages of the spectator role could be investigated in more depth by further research. For men the shifts over time between participating in and watching sport seemed to be closely bound up with their life stories and so might have particularly strong links with self-image and identity. Existing research suggests that in the absence of clear 'given' physical markers (equivalent to menstruation and the menopause in women) men may sensitise themselves to the relationship between their biography and their well-being through other means such as activity or the lack of it (Watson, 1993). This implies the need for more systematic research into gender differences in relation to sport and mental health.

# 4. Emotional support

Identifying and measuring supportive interventions and behaviour from a lay perspective remain problematic. Emotional support has been one subsumed element within a wider concept (Finch and Mason, 1993; Oakley and Rajan, 1991). For example, Oakley and Rajan identify emotional support as one of three elements, along with financial and instrumental support, which makes up their larger construct of 'social support'. However, it may be possible methodologically to identify emotional support as an entity in its own right, in order to map its relation to the wider construct of social support. One recent study which does attempt to measure the impact of emotional support, as a connected but distinct aspect of social support, is that by Wheelan (1993) which explores the role of the latter in mediating the social consequences of economic stress.

Another attempt to define and mark off emotional support from other forms of support is made here by Schaefer *et al.,* (1981):

> *Emotional* support includes intimacy and attachment, reassurance, and being able to confide in and rely on another – all of which contribute to the feeling that one is loved or cared about, or even that one is a member of the group, not a stranger. *Tangible* support involves direct aid or services and can include loans, gifts or money or goods, and provision of services such as taking care of needy persons or doing a chore for them. *Informational* support includes giving information and advice which could help a person solve a problem and providing feedback about how a person is doing.

It can be seen that, within this definition, emotional support implies inter-personal processes such as warmth, empathy, trust and reliable presence, whereas the other two notions, mentioned by Schaefer *et al.,* are more action orientated and could occur impersonally. However, in practice there is a fuzzy boundary between these three sub-concepts given the everyday evidence (confirmed at times by our respondents) that both tangible and informational support can have clear-cut positive emotional consequences. Because emotional support entails relationships it involves both a personal and social context. Whether viewed psychologically or sociologically it involves two sets of actors: those who give support (or undertake emotional labour – see below) and those who receive it.

Whilst social support has received quite considerable attention by social scientists over the last two decades – including the study of lay definitions – there has been less work on emotional support. Do people, for example, view emotional support in the manner envisaged above and, if so, what do such professional terms as, 'intimacy' 'attachment', 'reassurance' and 'confiding' mean to them? Lay knowledge in this area is likely to be complex. What little work has been done suggests that multiple realities are associated with these terms. For example, feeling that one is loved or cared about is a highly gendered construct. Lay knowledge reveals that men and women who choose to live together attach different meanings and expectations to notions of affection and care (Duncombe and Marsden, 1993). Other markers of emotional support used in existing research include: the range and involvement with social networks (friends, relatives); help received from domestic partners; and self-reported perceptions of support (Oakley *et al.*, 1994).

In our study, respondent assumptions* about privacy meant that we found that emotional support was not commonly reported. Confiding in friends by either the female or male respondents was rare and occurred with reservations.

Brown and Harris (1978) mention the presence of a close confiding relationship as a protective factor against depression. It was clear from our respondents that external and subjective markers of what constitutes intimacy do not always coincide. Descriptions of a degree of intimacy (for example, living with a husband who is seen as mentally healthy) may not translate into a confiding relationship. People do not necessarily confide in those they see as emotionally strong or mentally healthy. The array of characteristics associated with mental healthiness implies why this might be the case.

The respondents were asked to give examples of people who they construed to be mentally healthy. Examples given of female models included those who were seen to be single-minded and tenacious (for example, Bett Lynch from 'Coronation Street' and Margaret Thatcher). When men were mentioned other qualities were emphasised. Being contained and non-expressive were deemed to be signs of mental strength. Male models suggested with these features included the Pope and a number of the fathers of the female respondents.

One female respondent when asked to identify the person she deems to be psychologically healthy described her husband as emotionally strong. However, she seeks out her mother, who has had a breakdown, to confide in when support is needed. Similarly another mother with young children reported for years not having anyone to confide in until an acquaintance started to share her problems with her and then she consequently started with a gap of several months to use this women to disclose her own personal problems to. This might suggest that people who have had problems of their own but who are also receptive to others make better lay counsellors than those seen as being psychologically strong.

A number of accounts (from across all family types) expressed an ambivalence about intimacy and confiding. A close confiding relationship, especially amongst teenage girls, seemed to be crucial at times in maintaining a sense of well-being but was not always seen as essential when problems arose. Then, someone who would take their problem seriously was viewed as being more important who might not be a best or very close friend.

One aspect of the above complexity is an implicit distinction between psychological sharing with others (emotional support) and feeling good in the presence of others – which may be a feature of maintaining mental health. The latter might include 'having a good laugh'. To complicate matters further the emotional labour of others may not be experienced as being supportive. Caring about can be highly resented, for example when some of the teenage respondents did not look favourably on parental efforts in this regard.

## THE NEED FOR PRIVACY AND THE THREAT OF DISCLOSURE

The assumed correlation between social support and emotional support is complicated further by the ambiguities which respondents perceived about others in their lives. Others can represent potential sources of succour, support and advice at times. At other times, they may be seen as being unhelpfully interfering. Moreover, what makes people feel good does not always flow from relationships. Music, alcohol, food and watching television are all identified as sources that people look to, to positively change their mood. Additionally, a personal disclosure might risk a loss

* Emotional suppport relating specifically to teenagers is discussed in Chapter 7.

of face, which might add to, rather than mitigate, existing difficulties. This ambiguity seems to engender ambivalence from respondents about the usefulness of disclosing personal feelings and sharing problems. For example, one respondent who considered solving psychological problems as something one does alone describes 'interference from other people' as 'stopping you finding out what is wrong'. Disclosure was also seen as problematic at times because of fears of *amplifying* a problem. One woman talks about this in the context of postnatal depression and help-seeking and expresses the view that talking to somebody about it 'is making a big deal of it'.

Similarly here an Asian mother of teenagers describes the *stresses* of disclosing in an extended family system:

> I mean in our culture it's more sort of try to keep it in the family and get help within the family before you go to other channels, which I think is more stressful anyway ... I think it's more stressful because everybody gets involved and it becomes a major issue...

The provision of written information in different contexts was seen as useful for a variety of reasons. One woman expressed a preference for written information over personal contact with a professional which usually involved careful negotiation because she felt she had control over the material which she could refer to when and how she pleased. Written information sometimes provided reassurance. One woman, having experienced what she described as the 'baby blues', felt that she could refer to baby books which normalised the experience for her by describing the various stages and timescale of the problem. To take another example, the provision of information was viewed as an important backdrop in case problems arose – for example in relation to information on teenagers and drugs and alcohol.

## IMPLICATIONS ABOUT PRIVACY AND DISCLOSURE FOR MENTAL HEALTH PROMOTION

- Exhortations to share difficulties may not always be well received, whereas practical tips or positively recognising efforts to cope alone might be more acceptable.
- Written information may be an important source of emotional support independent of professional contact.
- Seeking help from others who have experienced problems of their own may be appealing for those who do want help. This implies that models such as co-counselling and self-help groups might be acceptable to people who lack these opportunities in their immediate social network.
- Recognition needs to be given to lay views about what keeps people emotionally healthy, including those that may clash with physical health promotion strategies such as promoting healthy lifestyles.
- The preference for resolving issues by oneself is mirrored and reinforced by the attitudes of health professionals to their clients and health promotion literature, which emphasises individual action and responsibility. This has sometimes been criticised for adopting a victim-blaming approach. An emphasis on individualism may be functional for most people most of the time and has the added advantage of fitting in with cultural norms of individualism which have proliferated in recent times. However, this may present problems for people who do not want to or cannot deal with problems on their own. If seeking help is seen as deviant and a weakness, it may reinforce personal distress.

## EMOTIONAL SUPPORT AND PROFESSIONALS

Implicit in The Health of the Nation's target reduction in suicide rates is the view that GPs are in a position to detect risk in vulnerable populations. However, the likelihood of implementing successful suicide prevention strategies within primary care has been questioned recently. A study of the case notes of adults dying by suicide found that medical contact near to the time of the suicidal act was rare (Matthews *et al.*, 1994). There has been concern that particular groups have less contact with GP services than the rest of the population and, moreover, that these groups may have more needs in relation to mental health and well-being than other groups in the population. There has been concern, for example, that black and minority ethnic groups (for a variety of reasons) have less contact with primary care services than other groups in the population (Pilgrim and Rogers, 1993). Additionally, teenager contact with GPs is less frequent, and consultation times shorter, than for other age groups in the population (Jacobson *et al.*, 1994).

The presentation and identification of emotional difficulties in primary care has also been a matter of debate. For example, liaison psychiatry has emphasised the importance of the recognition of the somatisation of emotional problems, i.e. the notion that those presenting with physical symptoms are in fact masking emotional problems. Particular groups, such as Asian women, are thought to be more vulnerable to this than others (Fenton and Sadiq, 1991).

However, there are some suggestions that somatisation might in part be a professional construction. One recent study found that those with an interest in liaison psychiatry use the diagnosis far more than those without liaison sessions (Stern *et al.*, 1993). Also, with regard to women, there is evidence that women's experience of minor physical disorder may 'cause' their higher rates of affective disorders (Popay *et al.*, 1993), rather than the latter being 'masked' by the former. Moreover, because health service use and positive outcome are not necessarily positively correlated, then it cannot be assumed that greater professional interest will lead to health gains. Low social class is associated with low social support but with high health service use. Consequently, health service use has been associated with an increased risk of adverse health outcomes among socially disadvantaged women. This has led some to claim that services which are not 'user friendly' may actually inflict an additional health burden on those who are already psychologically vulnerable (Oakley *et al.*, 1994).

### *Preference for social rather than medical support*

In the study reported here a number of accounts identified how GPs were viewed in relation to the seeking of emotional support. GPs were not the primary source of emotional support for most respondents. Although this varied according to gender, with men identifying the use of the GP for emotional support more frequently than women, the doctor's role was viewed as one dealing with medical rather than emotional problems. As one woman put it:

> If I was worried about something I could go and see my sister. If it was a medical problem, I'd see my doctor to get to the bottom of what was troubling me.

There was evidence of a clear preference for lay social support as opposed to medical support in dealing with emotional problems:

> At the moment I'm feeling quite down, I've been to court with my ex-husband and it was bad news really, and I went to see the doctor about it, and she's given me

> some anti-depressants, but I won't take them. What I will do is go and see my friends and tell them what's happened and why I feel down, tell everybody about it and get all the sympathy off them and it will help me. Not only that, I'll take my kids round with me to visit and they will play with the other kids...

When asked how taking the children round to friends helped, she said:

> You're not looking after them. You're not stuck in the house on your own with them. If you're feeling down and unable to cope, they're like an added burden to you. So if you take them somewhere it helps.

The GP's use to this women, from her perspective, was in providing a sick note. Thus, GP support is relevant but indirectly. It facilitates the conditions under which she can cope on her own or gain help from her lay network. This is consistent with the finding that patients with mental health problems prefer the facilitative role of GPs, which is a combination of an ordinary human response plus a 'fix-it' or gatekeeper intervention to enable access to material benefits (a sick note, a letter to the housing department, etc.) (Pilgrim and Rogers, 1993). Thus, what GPs are accessed for by their patients may not be emotional support but the 'tangible' support described by Schaefer *et al.*, (1981).

## IMPLICATIONS FOR MENTAL HEALTH PROMOTION

- The availability of professionals does not necessarily translate into client confidence in their provision of support. Because primary care professionals have the highest contact level with the general population this does not mean that service users experience them as sources of support. Despite the common assumption that GPs would be more effective if their psychiatric knowledge were increased and more emotional morbidity identified, from a service user's point of view ordinary relating and practical help may be more important. The way in which professionals are viewed and the support they provide is returned to under 'Maintaining mental health in the under 5s' in Chapter 6.

# 5. Mental health and family relationships

This chapter considers the ways in which inter- and intra-generational relationships affect the emotional lives of the respondents.

## CONFLICT IN FAMILIAL RELATIONSHIPS

Though harmonious relationships were seen as desirable, conflict was generally viewed as an inevitability of modern family life. Conflict was also viewed as a positive thing by some respondents, in the right amounts. An example of this is given by this respondent who discusses the issue of harmonious relationships within family life which reflects a protoprofessionalised position discussed in the section on defining and understanding mental health (note the emphasis added):

> Unhealthy harmony is where there is such a level of civility and everybody is being polite and there's *repressed conflict* that's not coming out. This might be *displaced* on to other things if there is just a total insistence on civil rules. It's a bit like the Weetabix family really. That to me is an unhealthy family relationship. Where it's chaotic – if people do tend to shout at each other, sometimes where people can *act out*... people feel safe to be the people they really are within the *family boundaries*.

Those holding this positive view about conflict saw rowing as a solution rather than as a problem in family life. It was also seen as a way of relating. When asked who her partner principally relates to this woman says:

> I think he probably talks more to me – probably argues more with me as well!

Conflict for some (but not others) was also viewed as a means of *strengthening* a relationship:

> I think sometimes the only way to test the strength of the bond is by pulling on it. Sometimes it's a bit like a tow rope, sometimes it's a way to give each other a hand. I think there are different ways of doing it. I think conflict is a way of challenging what somebody else does.

When conflict was viewed in a positive light this still had limits to it:

> I think it is healthy to release the aggression. It's unhealthy at times when you try to see how far you can go.

There were different types of conflict reported between adult partners. Some were considered petty or trivial, such as about what to watch on television. Sustained conflict or disaffection was considered more serious and was linked to thoughts in some respondents about separation. Examples of the latter focused on a partner not

meeting needs or paying enough personal attention over a long period of time.
Women were more likely to express the need to avoid conflict than men and would act to contain conflict as suggested here:

> I hate rows. I hate conflict. I would rather have a row with Mike than with the children or leave something as it is so as not to rock the boat ... Sometimes I'll keep quiet to try and avoid the conflict.

Tension was also reported to creep into relationships by different stances to conflict in the wake of arguments:

> He doesn't like arguments. He remembers them a lot longer than me as well. Once it's over with, it's over with ... I don't keep hold of it. But every now and then he'll come out with something I've said six years ago ...

## COMMUNICATION

As with conflict, the value placed on communication differed within the respondents. For some it was a necessity of everyday life, as indicated by this middle-class man:

> We talk when we get home from work, making tea or something. She will say 'this happened or he's a so-and-so'. That helps to get it out of you. It clears your mind, so you are not bottling it up.

Others did not see communication in itself as an important aspect of family life. Communication, it seems, is linked to closeness but from the accounts it was not possible to clarify whether people are close because they communicate well or they communicate because they have a pervasive sense of trusting intimacy in their partners. It is likely that they are two mutually reinforcing processes. There was a tendency for men to be less communicative than their female partners. Women were sometimes concerned that their male partners were 'bottling things up'. This, it seems, is linked to different expectations about what should be disclosed and to whom, as described here:

> There was an issue a few years ago where he got an appointment for the hospital for something and it was something he hadn't told me about. It was for something trivial. I can't think what it was. I think it was his teeth. So it was nothing that was secretive as such but ... it hadn't occurred to him that I might want to know about it. He probably doesn't want to worry me. The rows that we've had in the past have been about him not telling me things.

The communication and self-expression was something that did not appear to come naturally with men in the same way as it did with female respondents. Here a middle-class man talks about *learning* to be expressive and confiding:

> When you first get married ... I was very immature and I tended to be civil all the time and it was only as I got through life, with life experience, *we* realised that this was wrong and it was rather immature behaviour and that you have to learn to have confidence in one another and trust each other and then barriers come down.

The emphasis added about 'we' suggests that the insight described was negotiated with his partner or may even have been supplied by her.

Male teenagers generally seemed to communicate less than other family members and when they did this was not usually about personal issues. Communication patterns varied across families. In one working-class teenage family the mother reported writing notes to her children when she wanted to communicate with them and the teenage children reported never talking to either of their parents. The only communication seemed to be in the form of explosive rows between the father and the teenagers, which resulted in resentment from both parents:

> Father: I'm the one that's got to do the shouting and bawling ... I wish she'd be harder with them, but like I say it's me that's got to do it, so I'm the big bad wolf...
>
> Mother: When there's more than two of us there's tension. I'm waiting for one of them to say something and the other will snap at them, and I don't like it. But I don't say anything ... I'll probably go upstairs and leave them to it.

## CLOSENESS AND FAMILIAL TIES

The general cultural expectation reported was that families should be close. Family closeness was described in a variety of ways and involved a variety of familial alliances and allegiances. Here a respondent describes juggling commitments:

> I'm close to all of them equally but there's a case for the kids. We've devoted time for the kids collectively and individually, but there's also a case for devoting time for ourselves, just the two of us. And as individuals we go our separate ways and do different things and have different interests.

For some the absence of conflict was considered to be the essence of the closeness of a family:

> We don't argue really. I'm talking about all of us, sisters and that. We get on well really, which is good because I'm not an argumentative person.

Some respondents seemed to view the *expected* primary defining relationship in the family as between two adult partners, as indicated by this respondent. She notes that in practice the close relationships were between adult and child (or children) rather than between adults:

> I don't know, I don't think Frank and I are as together as some couples. You know some couples always do things together ... I think we're probably quite close with the kids...

She saw benefits in not being too close to her husband. She thought this distancing allowed her to get on and do things independently which she valued. Another middle-class respondent expressed similar reservation about closeness to her partner – 'I think you need to keep something for yourself'. These limits to closeness were not expressed by her middle-class male spouse.

A contrasting view is put by a middle-class woman who does prioritise her relationship to her husband believing that this has benefits for the whole family:

> Most importantly would be my relationship with Mat because otherwise if we are not happy together we are not as a family all happy then.

Whilst generally principal relationships were to be found either with partners or with children living at home, the exception to this was found in some of the interviews with working-class people interviewed in Liverpool. Here a mother living in a two-partner system with teenagers 'confesses' her priorities:

INTERVIEWER: In terms of people then in the family, do you have any priorities or does anyone come first?
RESPONDENT: Well, it's a terrible thing to say but my parents really are my main priority, I would bend over backwards to please my mother. She's a pain sometimes but rather than upset her you tend to say 'I'll go with my mother', or 'I'll take my mother shopping', or 'I'll do this with my mother'.

When asked the reasons for the prioritising of this relationship she puts this down to her mother's 'strong character and personality', her past relationship with her ('she was always there my mother') and 'looking after your own'.

Generally eldest children reported being closer to parents than younger siblings. If they were of the same sex, this was sometimes accounted for in terms of companionship and joint activities. Football is an example here. One father describes how he feels closer to one of his children because of this – 'I favour Chris because he's football and I'm football'. The significance of football and sport as a male emotional agenda echoes comments reported in Chapter 3, 'Maintaining mental health'.

Mutuality and fulfilling communication appears to be the basis for this mother – eldest son relationship:

> We have a good relationship, as I said before, he helps me a lot and I talk to him more than I talk to the others.

One notable difference between the working-class and middle-class accounts was that closeness in the family was sometimes described by the former in friendship terms. Here one mother accounts for her family's cohesiveness:

> We're friends. Me and Dave [her partner] have always been best mates anyway. We didn't want to just batter the kids and send them to bed. We wanted them to be friends with us. And we've always tried to keep friends. They know if they have a problem, they can talk to us about it. And they know that we'll do all we can to help them.

Contact was an important pre-condition for developing close relationships, as was time. Poor physical proximity to relatives was almost always seen as a barrier to developing more intimate relationships, whilst those with families living nearby tended to provide more inclusive notions of immediate family membership. Although proximity was an issue for all types of family, the concept of closeness was expressed more in working-class families as physically being and doing things together:

> I can't see us not being close. We go shopping together, we do everything together ... We go out together, we stay in together. The only thing we don't do is watch television together.

Here a working-class woman from Liverpool describes being close to female members of her family:

> We go anywhere together, days out, we go on holiday, it's always altogether, we

> have meetings at my mum's at least once or twice a week. And we're always on the phone to each other.

Whilst closeness was viewed as generally a positive thing to have, at times intimacy could be a source of stress for family members. This working-class father from Liverpool viewed sharing emotion in his family as problematic at times. He considered that his family was 'too close at times' and went on to give an example of the consequences of this:

> Like the other week when we dropped the eldest lad off (at college 150 miles away), coming home in the car one started crying and then they all did. I thought, 'bloody hell, this isn't on, this'. So, yes you do get too close ... It gets to you at times, you think you shouldn't really get upset that way, you should see it another way. He's making his own life now.

A few families described themselves as not being close. This was sometimes attributed to persistent conflict and non-communication. Sometimes families simply did not view themselves in those terms, e.g. 'we're not that kind of family who are the "relationship" kind'. The loss of closeness was also an issue which people were often unable to account for. Bemused accounts of this loss were more notable in the male accounts:

> I wouldn't have married Vera unless I loved her. But somewhere along the way something happened, I don't know what. I don't know where it happened, but it's not as close as it could be.

## IMPLICATIONS FOR MENTAL HEALTH PROMOTION

- Whilst the material about family relationships described by parents and teenagers was characterised on both sides by an emotional agenda, the latter was variable. Indeed, the differences between the respondents is reflected often in the wording of our text – 'some ...', 'sometimes', etc. The extensive literature from developmental psychology indicates that the transition to adulthood is variable and that adolescence is too often stereotyped as being about emotional storms – for many it is an unremarkable period in life. Our hope and intention was to construct a family typology of ways of negotiating relationships but the family member accounts we elicited did not then warrant this.

This point about lack of types of family relationships also applied to those between adults. Expectations about emotional closeness or ways of expressing aggression varied from family to family. Not only did reports of, say, intimacy and conflict vary but so did the attitude towards what was being described. As we noted, conflict is seen as healthy by some but not by others and even the former put caveats on their position.

There were some broad differences between social groups (although within these broad trends there was still considerable variability and overlap between the groups). Working-class families placed more of an emphasis on intimacy between all family members (not just parents), reflecting a notion of friendship. Also the Liverpool families seemed to be more family orientated in their lives than those from other localities. There are also apparent differences in the way in which men and women experience conflict and are expressive and communicative within the family.

Health promoters need to be aware of the differences in this regard in considering how their messages might best be targeted and received.

An implication of this variability is that there are no simple and standard mental health promotion messages which could be constructed for all families. Moreover, given the type of study reported, we do not know what mental health outcomes accrued from the variations in family life and attitudes reported.

# 6. Babies, toddlers and mental health

Parents' accounts support the truism about the birth of a child, namely that it brings in its wake a major disruption in all areas of life. What the accounts shed most light on is the nature and degree of the emotional upheaval that people experienced in terms of the disruption of existing relationships, particularly with partners, and their ways of managing these stresses.

## EMOTIONS AND RELATIONSHIPS AROUND BIRTH

The 'shock' of having a first baby was a salient theme in women's accounts of having children under 5. As one women put it, 'I wasn't very baby-like so it's a severe shock to the system.' Another used an economic metaphor to express how she felt. 'You get a bit of a battering when you have a baby . . . I was dead fit until I had her. I was still decorating the day before, then the day afterwards I was in severe recession.' This experience of emotions and shock was not reported to the same extent in the interviews with men. Though they acknowledged changes, these were more to do with changes in lifestyles or habits than with relationships or emotions. For example, in response to the question, 'And when they were born were there any great emotional changes either for yourself or your wife?', this man responded 'Not emotionally, no. A disruption of our activity but not emotionally, no.'

With regard to relationships, most women reported a change in priorities. The latter shifted from their partner to the baby. This change was rarely the focus of an explicit agreement or conversation but is something that happened with the arrival of a child. At times it was noted by women that there had been no discussion about the changing nature of their relationships with their partners – it just seemed to happen automatically. These changing priorities were seen as a challenge, as indicated by this middle-class mother:

> When they are babies you have to put them first, because they are physically dependent. I think that's a problem for lots of people when the kids are born, and their husbands are really jealous of them. Because he was always a bit funny when they were born and I didn't really identify it. He was a bit funny with them, but it was all right, it settled down. But at the beginning I think that's because you're giving them all the attention, particularly the first one.

The attempts to involve men in child care, more particularly the birth, also seems at time to invoke mixed feelings on the part of women. This ambivalence seems to stem from the fact that physically and emotionally men are not in the same position as a pregnant/birthing woman. Also men do not generally participate in the care of the child in the same way as the mother:

> I mean they [men] are not going through it in the same way as you are, because you've carried this thing for nine months. Some men are in there doing your

> breathing exercises. And I wouldn't really like that because I think they are trying to take over the nice bits and not doing the grotty bits. I mean he didn't change nappies but he would take them for walks.

Rather than this being seen wholly as a negative thing this respondent goes on to indicate that she guarded her rights and work in this area jealously:

> In a way I didn't mind, because I wanted them to be mine. So maybe I'm selfish too. I used to look at them, I breast-fed them for four months, and they'd eaten nothing. I thought I made them grow from that to that, all on my own. I felt I'd achieved something.

If these feelings of achievement and 'ownership' are typical, it may go some way to shedding light on the contradictory finding in recent research that women describe their partners as being supportive during pregnancy and around birth even though their participation in child care chores is often not great (Oakley and Rajan, 1991). The division of labour may be negotiated with advantages to both parents, rather than it necessarily being only about men avoiding tasks. A feature of the changes in relationships taking place between partners was that frequently people were unaware of the impact of the birth until sometime later. An example of this is given by one of the male respondents here:

> We found that we were having a lot of aggressive rows with each other. Which in retrospect you look at and think 'it's the stress of the whole situation', but at the time ... If you were a totally together person you'd realise that you were responding to your emotions. At the time stresses were coming because of the stress of the disturbance and normal routines – family life, the upset, visiting the hospital and people's needs weren't being met and there was a disturbance of the equilibrium.

Clearly not all births have the same significance and impact on existing relationships. After the first child the births of subsequent children were reported as being less traumatic in terms of the disruption of an existing dyadic relationship with a partner. None the less, other issues may assume importance, such as negotiating the introduction of a sibling to an existing child. Here, one mother describes her awareness of the trauma the impending birth of her second child might have had on her first and the strategies she used to manage the risk:

> Well, seeing other friends with their children and babies coming along, they get jealous, throwing tantrums and behaving badly or just not being happy. So I think consciously I made sure that he started at nursery quite a few months before the baby was due and we moved the bedrooms. Three or four months before we got him potty trained, quite some time before the baby was due. Because I thought if you try and do it nearer the time then he was just going to think 'they're just packing me off to nursery or they take me out of that bedroom and move my bedroom and put the baby in that bedroom' ... We were aware there could be problems so we sort of thought about the eventualities to make it as easy as possible for the adjustment.

## MATERNITY CARE

Negative experiences of how pregnancy and birth were managed by professionals were seen as having important emotional consequences. Women not having a choice is an example:

> I would have liked a home birth but they didn't do them, and with being 34 it was out of the question. I was a high-risk mother or so I was told . . . The doctor said he would have a word with the consultant and in the afternoon he rang me up and said it wouldn't be possible and that made me mentally a bit down.

Here a father contrasted the positive experiences and feelings he had around the birth of two of his children with the third:

INTERVIEWER: Were there any psychological issues that you can remember around the time of the birth which are important for you when your children were born?

RESPONDENT: Yes, the one that springs to mind is the negative feelings towards the institutions when our children were born, just the one child in particular, David who is the middle child. June went into labour and she had high blood pressure. It wasn't a serious business but the attitude of the hospital was so appalling all the way through. Funnily enough, I found myself having negative feelings towards the child when he was born. It was only in retrospect that you recognise this, and how a good birth helps you, even a man, bond more readily than when you get a really awful institutional birth it can have a bad effect on you. It doesn't help you start off very well.

At times it seems hospitals can make a bad situation much worse. One woman describes how through a 'medical mistake' she was informed that her child had Down's Syndrome and how this was 'badly' dealt with. Here she describes her reaction to the hospital staff:

> I was annoyed because they actually, without asking me, seemed to diagnose what they thought my mental state was going to be that evening and removed her from me. So they actually caused more stress by, yet again, following textbook procedure on how I was going to react and did the most stressful thing possible and removed the child from me . . . I actually had to almost physically fight to get my child out of the nursery. They had actually moved her into a corner physically away from the rest of the babies which made me feel even more isolated. So, hand on heart, what should be a caring professional safe haven actually became very threatening, very confusing to me and I actually probably would have been better to have been in the love and comfort of my own home with my family around me.

There were also indications that contemporary antenatal care and advice about pregnancy and birth fail to address adequately the emotional reality of having a baby and attendant tasks surrounding baby care:

RESPONDENT: I read a lot of books, then I went to everything, parenting classes, everything . . . they were useful but I don't think anything really prepares you – nothing like the real shock of things.

INTERVIEWER: What kinds of things do you think you are not prepared for?

RESPONDENT: Well, they show how to bath a plastic doll but you've never done it, you've never picked up a new-born baby – it's all well and good saying do this, do that, but at the time it's different. Until you've been in a situation you wouldn't imagine that something, like you don't get on with breast feeding, was a big challenge. But when it happens to you, you realise, it's bigger than all the projects you've set at work in fifteen years of working. Because it's about a person that you're responsible for.

For some mothers the onslaught of advice and information about pregnancy, child birth and early child rearing was difficult to deal with and was sometimes viewed as an extra emotional burden at a time when they least wanted it. The popularisation of health information, which is widely disseminated in the media and particularly aimed at women, examines and advises on every aspect of pregnancy and childbirth. The lack of training and education in becoming parents has been a popular theme in recent years. But within this discourse there has been a tendency for the notion of support to be combined with education (Edwards, 1995). Thus parents might not necessarily view such information as necessarily helpful – education may be experienced as a hindrance rather than a support. However, generally in the accounts given by mothers, information was seen as useful. The proliferation of information was acknowledged as a significant trend by a number of mothers. Written material appeared to be used by mothers having second or third babies as a form of 'revision', in preference to using formal antenatal classes. However, the amount and nature of information available sometimes led to feelings of confusion and guilt in mothers for not following advice or not knowing *which* advice to follow.

Pregnancy surveillance and foetal diagnostic tests, although acknowledged at one level as being beneficial, could also engender anxiety. A mother here discusses the changes in information advice and surveillance in the six years since her last pregnancy:

RESPONDENT: There's more tests and things available now. Also this big thing about what not to eat. When I had my first there was nothing I shouldn't eat that could harm your baby, now it seems everything can.

INTERVIEWER: Does this information have an effect on you?

RESPONDENT: Its good in one way but in others it panics you a bit, you know the triple test and that. The result I got was high risk to have a Down's baby. It's not a reliable test and in the end the baby is normal. I wish I'd never had the test. It's worried me for the whole of my pregnancy.

Parents also contrasted the amount and nature of information *prior* to the birth with a dearth of information and realistic support afterwards. The provision of information to use after the arrival of the baby may be most effectively delivered postnatally, as people may find it difficult to project themselves into a position where they may need support and advice. Here a mother describes the 'unreality' of postnatal depression prior to the birth of her child:

INTERVIEWER: Did the parentcraft class tell you anything about how you may feel after the birth – postnatal depression, for example?

RESPONDENT: Not very much, they did touch on it. The thing is you don't really want to know. You know, you are not sitting there thinking, 'I'm going to have postnatal depression in six weeks' time.' I think in a lot of people it's a capacity for sticking your head in the sand really.

Parents often alluded to the fact there were networks of breast-feeding counsellors but remained reluctant or unsure about how to access these. One young working-class mother said:

> There was an awful lot [of information] while you're pregnant and then you're in labour, but there was nothing afterwards. Like I suppose there was postnatal classes at the hospital, but if you're suffering from postnatal depression you are not going to go to the hospital.

Sometimes professionals were perceived as assuming that some types of mothers did not require support. One mother, whose husband was a gynaecologist, reports that it was presumed she knew everything when, in fact, as she pointed out, he knew 'nothing about babies!'

Informal support from other mothers, when it was mentioned, was deemed to be both relevant and desirable. For example, one mother described feeling petrified about cot death and unable to deal with her child's sleeping pattern. Having struggled with these issues on her own for sometime, she reported that her fear of cot death subsided and her ability to cope with her child's sleeplessness improved after talking about these things to other mothers. Similarly, mothers emphasised the importance of getting together with other mothers and their babies.

## IMPLICATIONS FOR MENTAL HEALTH POLICY OF DATA ON MATERNITY CARE

- Antenatal classes should try to give more of a sense of the *experience* of having a new born baby. Bathing and other advice may be better coming from women who have just had a baby. This might inspire confidence in women about to give birth and give women who have just had a baby a sense of worth and self-confidence. Also the 'shock' and disruption to existing intimate relationships (particularly with live-in partners) needs to be given greater prominence in antenatal information and education.
- The negative emotional impact of health surveillance during pregnancy needs to be acknowledged by healthcare workers. It should also be considered whether better targeting of techniques for those at risk during pregnancy might reduce the need for surveillance in all expectant mothers. Mass screening may not be a cost-effective health promotion intervention if it generates lasting iatrogenic anxiety in those women who are likely to produce healthy babies.
- Information is useful and wanted – but the way that it is delivered is very important for the self-esteem of parents. Professionals giving advice should take into account the way it is likely to be received. At times the need of parents to feel supported may take precedence over compliance with the content of advice. Advice about postnatal issues may not be well used antenatally. Thus the timing and manner of information transfer is as important as its content.

## INTERVENTIONS FROM HEALTH VISITORS AND OTHER PROFESSIONALS

When discussing issues concerning emotional support in under 5s, one woman reported that the most helpful thing to her was a GP who inspired confidence by one comment. This was that if she was ever concerned about her child in any way she should never sit at home worrying about it but should bring the child to the surgery. This had the effect of providing a supportive backdrop if the woman ever needed it – she says in fact she thought she used the GP *less* because of this.

Equally as important is the way in which health visitors (HVs) are perceived by our respondents. At times of crises it seems that health visitors and midwives may well act as useful forms of emotional support. The positive impact of appropriately targeted social support has been shown by a number of recent studies. A recent longitudinal study (Oakley *et al.,* 1994) showed that the impact of positive social support postnatally can have an effect on the emotional and physical well-being of children seven years after birth. However, this was predicated on a trial in which HVs allow the control and agenda to stay firmly rooted in the mothers' hands. Some mothers' accounts in this study indicated that the physical well-being of the child was what dominated the usually brief and cursory contact people had with HVs. The tests and physical check-ups and developmental tests were what predominated. As with prenatal tests, a question is begged about whether parents experience surveillance as helpful and supportive or whether it may also create insecurity.

Usually HVs are viewed as having a fairly marginal role to play in events around childbirth. Most women viewed becoming a mother as relying on learning from partners and others and from their own emerging experience. However, at times HVs seemed to take on a more important role when providing the support and help which is sometimes absent from parents' own networks. One respondent said she classed her HV 'as a friend of the family' and noted in particular her accessibility and concern for other members of the family other than the children.

Here a women describes feeling down after having a baby and how the HV intervened. A working-class woman, who in other parts describes herself as not being aware of things going on around her and admits her failure to get through to people, gives the following account:

INTERVIEWER: So for you the support from the HV was really important?
RESPONDENT: Yes, because it had been a really bad breakdown, and it was Susan, my health visitor, who just took one look at me and said 'you need help'. She went away and ten minutes later she was on the phone to say she had Tom a place in the nursery ... I remember my mum sitting here and saying to my health visitor, 'I come down everyday, I help her'. It was a load of crap, but I sat there and didn't say anything and it's only now when I look back that I think bloody hell!

Here a woman describes the importance of the support provided by a midwife when breast-feeding became difficult emotionally and physically. She felt herself 'sinking lower and lower' after each feed but persevered because of 'peer and personal pressure':

> There was a midwife who befriended me, who used to come out once a week. I think she could see the warning lights and every time she came I was in tears about one breast-feeding episode or another, and she started talking to me, saying I was not making myself happy, and you're going to sink lower and lower.

However, not everyone appreciated the intervention of HVs and some actually perceived them as a source of emotional stress. A middle-class woman saw HVs as a potential source of distress and an undermining influence on her ability to cope as an informed parent. This seems to be related to a sense of inner confidence which may relate to class. This women describes how HVs dealt with her having a large baby:

> They tend to overreact quite a lot. I felt that deep down that I was doing the right things and I knew that I wasn't giving him sweets, I wasn't giving him sugary drinks, I was making food at home, purée and all that, doing what I thought was the right thing to do. Every time I went to get him weighed it was 'God, what are you feeding him, you're feeding him too much and you've got to stop him having milk, reduce this, reduce that, we ought to refer you to a dietitian for advice...'

> They made you think there was something wrong with you even though he was reaching his milestones ... I used to come home feeling really upset by it, I just thought I'm not doing anything wrong, he was born big and he is a huge big baby but I'm doing all I can.

She describes her subsequent interaction:

> When I take him down now they say 'Gosh, he's thinned down, I knew it would happen. I knew as soon as he walked'. And I think 'No you didn't because you used to harass me the whole time.'

She reported feeling angry with HVs and more confident in looking at books or using her own initiative. Another respondent describes how she resented the intrusion of HVs into her home:

RESPONDENT: I have an aversion to health visitors, I don't let them in the house.
INTERVIEWER: Why don't you let them in the house?
RESPONDENT: Well the first one that walked into my house, we lived in [a northern town] and it was the middle of winter when my daughter was a few weeks old. 'This child will die in here, it's too cold', that sort of thing. I think people coming into the family on a health basis sometimes cause more trouble than they are worth ... I'd say with all the children there was always some sort of physical thing that crops up with babies and instead of somebody being there and supporting you and saying 'Oh it will be all right', to come in and say 'Oh my God!', it's not very helpful. I don't think they realise the damage they do.

Resentment was also expressed about the *non-negotiated* aspects of HV intervention – such as visits which were not invited by the mother and 'being told what to do'.

## IMPLICATIONS FOR MENTAL HEALTH PROMOTION OF DATA ON HEALTH VISITORS

- Parenting skills are seen as central to professionals' views of what parents should be doing for their children. Recent research suggests that these professional notions centre on issues to do with development – emphasising, for example, stimulation and loving environments. Although, as Dingwall and Robinson (1990) found, health visitors' encounters with new mothers are 'not used to conduct any clear and systematic health assessment or health education'. Parental needs were rarely recognised by professionals (Edwards, 1995). Health professionals' views are also likely to screen out those structural issues which, although recognised as important, are out of their control. Consequently, such issues as poverty (the key social determinants of mental health identified by respondents) are largely absent from their interactions with parents. However, health visitors are involved in ameliorative 'fringe' activities with clients, which are helpful, if arguably paternalistic (de la Cuesta, 1993). The views about causes of mental healthiness examined in other parts of this report suggest that from a parental viewpoint, structural questions of finance, employment and environment are salient or overriding issues in relation to mental health and well-being. Thus a mismatch between professional and lay discourses may not make communication easy. Ignoring these factors in communications between parents and mental health professionals suggests that the ground rules for effective communication and understanding may from the outset be jeopardised.

- The model of working used by antenatal health workers would seem to be important in providing *appropriate* emotional and social support for families with young children. Oakley (1988) notes that the 'care' and support element, which was a starting point for professional principles and practice of antenatal care, has gradually been transformed over a 30-year period to a point where it has taken on the 'character of a technological surveillance programme'. Moreover, whilst expressed needs are more acknowledged in what Dingwall and Robinson (1990) term 'the new health visiting', views expressed from a lay perspective are marginalised by an epidemiological definition of need which, 'will now start from the official picture of the community and seek to find the individuals who fit its categories' (p. 268). There is some indication that a different model, which focuses on providing social and emotional support to mothers is more acceptable and effective. One such model of social support in pregnancy and around birth which has been effective in promoting physical and psychological health gain in mothers and their babies is that devised by Oakley *et al.* (1994). A social support programme aimed at disadvantaged mothers was devised which mimicked, to a large extent, informal support that might be provided by a well established friendship network or informal systems provided by voluntary organisations, such as the National Childbirth Trust. A service was devised and provided by midwives. This included the following elements: a 24-hour contact telephone; a programme of home visits during which the workers provided a 'listening' service; practical information and advice when asked; referral on to other health professionals and welfare agencies as appropriate; and the collation of medical and social information. In addition to significant health gain, the participating women's attitudes to the social support intervention were very positive. The fact that midwives were prepared to listen was singled out as the most important factor.

An implication of this for health visitors is that the traditional surveillance emphasis is not compatible with one which focuses on the experiences and expressed needs of parents and a brokerage model in which the health visitor mobilises aspects of the immediate social context in the interests of vulnerable individuals.

## MAINTAINING MENTAL HEALTH WHEN LOOKING AFTER YOUNG CHILDREN

The impact of children on people's previous relationships was acknowledged by a number of interviewees. Some tried hard to preserve a pre-existing relationship with their partner independently of their children. This was important when both partners perceived themselves to have a strong relationship. For those where there was disharmony and where there had been emotional problems then external support was seen as crucial. Groups and nurseries perform that function of giving validity that is otherwise obtained from a parent's or partner's inner resources.

At times the *emotional* support gained by parents from contact with organised external activities is difficult to disclose. A surface account would thus emphasise the practical aim of a group meeting but the subjective gain may not be readily confessed:

> When I had Sarah I thought I had to keep sane, and they had a mother and baby group so I went there once and I thought there's more to the world than babies . . . but I went there for my brain but all these other ones went there for the babies.

An implication of this preference for privacy about emotional life is that to explicitly emphasise and openly acknowledge the mental health enhancing qualities of organised childcare activities might be counterproductive. However, in terms of mental health promotion it seems crucial that primary care nurses are sensitive to the support for mothers that such activities provide and should be targeting and arranging such activities for them. This is reinforced by the literature which emphasises that such activities are crucial in preventing depression amongst women (see, for example, Jennifer Newton's *Preventing Mental Illness in Practice,* 1992).

## MAINTAINING MENTAL HEALTH IN THE UNDER 5s

Views on who should be responsible for a child's mental health tended to differ according to the employment status of parents. Working parents in two-partner families tended to say that the responsibility was shared and that issues were discussed as they arose. When the woman worked part-time, or not at all, then she tended to take the main responsibility. Single parents saw themselves as solely responsible, although they tried to dilute this by bringing in extended family members if they were available.

Some parents considered the issues of the psychological or emotional well-being of their children prior to their birth. An account from one set of parents, who rationally appraised their suitability as 'good enough' parents after an unexpected pregnancy, is given here:

> Because he wasn't planned, it was a surprise. We decided that we were stable enough and could give him a good upbringing.

Parents focused on honesty and authentic mutual disclosure in a supportive atmosphere with their children as a factor which engendered mental healthiness. One element of disclosure for this parent was that of demonstrating loving feelings. She was asked what contributes to mental health:

> Well, I would say 'love'. I don't mean in a gushy sense, I mean loving them bad or good – making then feel good really, supporting their decisions if you are talking about children and hopefully putting across that you love them no matter what they do. That they feel that they've got somebody to go back to when they mess everything up. I mean from being this high [points level hand] that's ongoing. I don't think that when we are adult we are any different. We still look to other people for approval. We still need that support...

Talking to children and providing stable security was another aspect mentioned. Protecting children from the rows and arguments was also mentioned, as was ensuring that siblings were given equal regard. Parental ability to assist and participate in the expression of feelings was also viewed as helping with the establishment of a healthy emotional life:

> He's very loving – affectionate to us and we encourage that a lot. He shows his feelings. He can talk about them now more, so he says whether he wants you to go near him or not. I just think it important that we all show affection.

Single parents, in particular, mentioned the impact of divorce or separation on their children, although this was usually seen as *temporary.* The impact was thought to recede once the disruption of splitting up had actually taken place. Subsequently, a child's contact with an ex-partner could be seen to pose problems over their psychological health. One lone mother stopped her child seeing her father until he had sought professional help for his 'mental instability', because of what she viewed as his inappropriate attitude. She reported that her ex-partner was unable to put the interests and needs of their three-year-old child first and that he tried to form an alliance with the daughter to reject her:

> If we're arguing or something and I'm saying to Nina, go outside and play with your friends, he has on occasion brought her back into the house to see me lose my temper with him ... I don't know if he's doing it intentionally, trying to get sympathy from her maybe. If I said to him 'For God's sake, just go away', he'd say 'Come on Nina, mummy doesn't want us.' Which I think is a horrible thing to say.

The lack of a partner meant re-adjusting the way in which lone parents supported their children. At times lone parents felt the need to be committed fully to their child's needs:

> She just needs to know that I'm there for her no matter what happens, again stability and security. She just has to be able to trust me 100 per cent.

Another single parent expressed the need to involve other members of the family:

> Well, it gives them confidence, doesn't it? You know that they've actually got somebody else there that they know they can go to if they don't really want to come and see me.

All parents tended to express the need for love, stability and security for their children. Differences between parents were a matter of emphasis rather than substantive content. Accounts from middle-class parents seemed to be more formulated about the emotional lives of their children. Stimulation and free expression were issues that were more likely to be expressed by middle-class rather than working-class parents. This mother is clear that free expression, interaction and stimulation with other children, and sufficient one-to-one time with them, are necessary for positive emotional development:

> I think if you want them to be normal and healthy, you've not got to suppress them. You've just got to let them behave like children, and not forget they are not adults. And do all the normal things we did as children. Mark gets a far more interesting stimulating life really because he's meeting a lot of other children ... He has a one-to-one relationship with the nanny, which I think is far more important than him going to a nursery. So at least he can use Jenny (the nanny) as a substitute mother.

Middle-class accounts tended to emphasise the need to protect children from parents' own problems or fights. Some accounts from working-class parents were more circumspect, in this regard, stressing the need to protect children but at the same time exposing them to adult problems, as indicated by this respondent:

> I mean kids shouldn't be privy to all adult emotions but on the other hand adult emotions shouldn't be hidden from them either. I think there has got to be a balance there because it helps them later in life if they've seen stuff.

## DISCIPLINE

Although at first sight this topic does not relate directly to the issue of mental health, the parental accounts about their discipline policies with their pre-school children produced a range of related issues. First, they placed discipline within an idiosyncratic personal context of emotions and power, which, for example, cannot be a consideration in nurseries or in child-minding arrangements, which have to be subject to standard policies. For example, this mother is talking of how she smacks her daughter only occasionally:

> Well if I did lose my temper with her then we always make a point of making up, when she's calmed down. She always comes and says, 'Sorry mummy'. I cuddle her and we always make up. It's very rare that she goes to sleep and I've been cross with her and we've not made up.

Secondly, such a personal context also entails parents with more than one child tailoring tactics for each. For example, this father is talking of the difference between his son and daughter and the need to read the dynamics within the family:

> Ben has always been a daddy's little boy ... I don't really have to shout at him, I just have to say 'don't do whatever'. Kate is a free spirit and I can see trouble ahead. When Jill [the wife] is here its absolutely murder to get her to bed. She cries and whinges because she wants Jill to be upstairs with her. But as soon as Jill is at work ... our Kate's as good as gold...

A third theme was the strain of trying to avoid physical punishment. Those parents who worried about this eschewed smacking, restricted it to being a last resort or acknowledged that circumstances might drive them to the practice:

> I don't think I'd want to be a smacker but I might change given the situation – but it would be an impulse thing. It wouldn't be 'I'll smack you when I get you downstairs, you naughty boy.' Slap on the back of the leg, which is what I had.

And another mother comments:

> I've always said I'd never smack my kids but I've started that now. Not really bad, you know. The odd slap on the hand and that. But it depends what he does. There's certain things. Like I'll tell him he won't touch anything in here, for example. Or if he goes on to he will test me every now and again. But I'll tell him about three times and if he doesn't [desist] I'll give him a little smack on his hand. Say he's going to touch the iron or something, I won't smack him for that. I'll try to say 'It's hot!' In other words, try to talk him through it.

This struggle to avoid smacking was recognised by some respondents as being linked not only to the pragmatic question of its effectiveness but the moral question of adult violence against children. Smacking thus entailed the experience of mixed emotions in parents of guilt and anger. Its close link in the mind of this respondent with violence is clear:

> Well, I think it [smacking] is wrong, really. It's the thin end of the wedge. If somebody sees me smacking my daughter and I see them smacking her what can I do about it? At the moment if I see anybody smacking my daughter I'll thump them.

A fourth and separate theme was that of instilling a moral sense in the child which will lead to a healthy outcome in their development. For example, this father comments:

> We try, though we are not always successful, to get her into bed by 8 o'clock and we do try and give her some kind of routine. No snacks before food. And she goes to nursery everyday which is discipline in itself really. We try to be firm and fair...

A surface reading of these responses is that they merely describe or constitute parental ideologies about maintaining order in the family or beliefs about the correct way to raise children. However, the elaborated and unintended content of these responses also revealed deeper issues of power and emotions. For some respondents the topic of discipline became the main vehicle to discuss emotional issues or questions of power between generations or between male and female parents. Proportionally, the issue of discipline in relation to teenagers and the under 5s took up a greater length of time than any other issue explored in the interviews. An example is given here of the interplay between power and feelings which are bound up with the topic of discipline:

> It should be me [responsible for discipline] because at the end of the day it's me who's got them 24 hours a day, especially with Damion working away a lot. But we are at loggerheads at the moment because I don't agree with smacking. I'm dead set against smacking... but Damion doesn't think anything of coming in and smacking them and we're arguing at the moment because if he's here and I'm telling them off, rather than let me sort them out he'll come in and smack them...

She goes on to talk about the effect that this clash over discipline might have on her child:

> Dad is smacking him, but now he's got in school – state run nursery and they have a policy of no smacking which is a good thing because I've got them backing me up as well... [but] it's confusing for him, really confusing, he's going to end up twisted if we don't make a decision soon.

This issue of hidden power relations and their implications is discussed further in Chapter 7 in relation to teenagers.

## MENTAL HEALTH PROMOTION INDICATIONS OF PARENTAL VIEWS ON DISCIPLINE

- The accounts about discipline have implications for mental health in three senses. First, parents believe that their discipline policy can affect the stability of their children by positively socialising them into acceptable habits. Secondly, some parents consider that physical punishment is unhealthy for their child's well-being and psychological development. Thirdly, the strain of deciding how to discipline children itself constitutes a source of stress for parents. Given that the dilemmas about discipline recur for all parents, the question of support and discussion (rather than education) returns (see preceding discussion).

# 7. Teenagers, mental health and health promotion

This chapter examines aspects of mental health in teenagers with reference to familial culture. Attention is given to: teenagers' views on emotional support (its meanings and sources); friendships; and family relationships. Subsequently, parental views on the following are examined: discipline; teenage development; risk-taking behaviour; and education.

## GROWING UP AND GROWING AWAY

The process of *distancing* between parents and teenage children was a prominent theme when both parties discussed family relationships. Prior closeness was eroded or lessened, as time passed. This loosening of familial ties entailing a gradual psychological and physical separation between the generations (or 'breaking away', as some described it) was reflected in changing family activities. As the children increased in age during adolescence, typically families ceased to share meals together as frequently as they used to. This tended to be justified with reference to the differing interests and commitments of family members. For some respondents, the importance of the remaining shared meals was heightened. It became a retained symbol of collective family life, when in other respects the latter was being eroded or destabilised. Such meals also provided an opportunity for communication with children who were spending more and more time with their peers. A further indication of this process of distancing was the curtailing or cessation of previously undertaken shared leisure, such as, for middle-class families, walking. This tended to be expressed by teenagers in terms of specific activities that were now abandoned, along with an expressed disaffection, such as describing them as 'boring'. From the adults' point of view this was seen in a wider sense, e.g. 'I feel we are losing touch with the older two'. Sometimes this was expressed in terms of loss. 'They obviously have their own lives and they don't want us as close. But certainly physically I think we've lost something'.

Some parents experienced a distancing from their teenage children in terms of a breakdown in sympathy and a mutual incredulity. Two examples are given of this, first from a middle-class mother of teenagers and then from a working-class father:

> I think even at 15 they are very experiential learners. You can't tell them. I'm sure my mother said this to me and I'm sure it goes round in generations. But I don't think teenagers really realise how immature they are and it's a very difficult concept to put across. They won't believe you if you tell them anything and they do such strange things. And you think 'why don't they listen?' and then they'll come back to you later and say 'you were right'. But I don't think you can really change what they do. They decide themselves. They are like programmed to do it.

> You can't advise them. They're going clubbing it, coming home at God knows what hour. We're in bed fast asleep. As I say, they get into their teens and you cannot talk to them. Especially girls.

Notions of the need for privacy were seen by parents as justifiable in terms of teenage withdrawal or cutting off. This distancing from parents is accompanied by an apparent growing importance of relationships with peers, as indicated by this father's account of his teenage son:

> At one time he was very family-orientated, whereas now there is peer pressure on him to move away from the family. He's a bit torn. He's torn between loyalties – between the two things.

Teenagers' accounts confirmed this shifting focus. Peers gained increasing importance as intimates and they increasingly substituted for parental relationships. Peers were viewed as understanding the teenage respondents' experience ('knowing you better'). This applied to both boys and girls but parents reported that the latter retained more personal contact than the former. As one mother put it, 'you get more off girls that you would say your son'. Parents at times viewed teenagers as non-rational and, in their view, this triggered conflict and led to the failure to resolve disputes at times. Here a mother describes an interaction with her teenage son about his sister:

> I'd done something for Janet which he didn't think I'd do for him. And he won't listen to me saying that I've done this, that and the other. He says, 'you would say that!' You can't really reason with them as you can adults . . . I could reason with you. Because you'd listen and I'd listen to you. But children don't necessarily obey those rules, so it's hard.

The importance of peer group conformity and normative social values, was also the focus of discussion and conflict between adults and teenagers. Here one mother reports her teenage daughter complaining that she is denied what her peers have:

> Michelle at the moment is at the stage of 'everybody else gets everything and we get nothing. Why do we never go abroad?' . . . Her temper tantrums, well her sulks basically, mainly revolve about her wanting things that she can't have.

When faced with these types of disgruntled response from teenagers parents tried a number of strategies. Sometimes they tried to persuade their children that, in the case of material things, other families have fewer children or more money. They also tried to appeal to anti-materialistic values – 'life isn't just about that' – trying to give her the non-materialistic point of view. However, this strategy was used with a faint heart but vague optimism – 'I don't really expect her to latch on at her age, just to keep her in check a bit'. Another strategy was one of 'count your blessings', when they reminded their children of other families where the parents were considered more disciplinarian. One result of this problem-solving in the case of grumpy teenagers was that parents were obliged to collaborate and consult in their own interests. In turn this might trigger a consultative approach to their negotiations with the children themselves. At other times though it could lead to the parents allying themselves against the 'teenager as enemy'.

However, the accounts from both parents and teenage children also contained examples of harmony and mutual respect. Adolescence was not seen as a problematic issue much of the time. Teenagers who described getting on with parents indicated a recognition of mutuality, as indicated by this teenage girl in discussing why she gets on well with her parents:

> They just let me do what I want to do, and I can see what they tell me not to do is reasonable, because they would have left me do it if it was OK.

There was also evidence that with increasing child–parent separation, some parents tried to foster a new relationship. Sandra, a single mother, had tried to be more of a friend than a disciplining parent to her daughter over time. She and her 18-year-old daughter were attempting to form a new relationship:

> I'm not used to being disagreed with. She has her own thoughts and I don't always agree with the way she tries to answer back . . . The stress comes from me not being able to talk to her . . . it's like having a battle, but she'll go away and think about it and I go away and think about it and we end up talking.

Sandra tried not to criticise her daughter's friends, so as not to harm their relationship or discourage her daughter from coming to talk to her about problems. A failure to appreciate a more distant relationship and a new identity was sometimes a problem. One teenager described his mother's attitude to girlfriends, which he attributed to her jealousy:

> She's always going on about every girl I've been out with . . . she doesn't like them, she doesn't blank them, but she doesn't make conversation with them.

He also complained about his sister's lack of appreciation for his need for privacy and personal space:

> Sometimes I come in and she's in my bedroom watching the telly and the video . . . it does my head in.

## FRIENDS AND EMOTIONAL SUPPORT

Respondents' accounts suggest that a principal source of emotional support for teenagers is their friends. A preference for friends replacing parents as sources of emotional support was sometimes evident. Friends were frequently identified as being the person a teenager would approach first although with very serious problems parents were usually viewed as the first port of call, as suggested by this teenage girl:

INTERVIEWER: Who would you go to if you had a big problem ?
RESPONDENT: Probably one of my friends actually. And then my mum, it depends on how big it was. If it was a really massive one, I'd probably go to my mum.

Accounts of differing expectations about communicating problems were frequently mentioned from teenage family members. Parental accounts expressed disquiet or perplexity about the failure of their teenage children to talk to them. For teenagers this failure was frequently normalised:

RESPONDENT: I talk to my friends, not necessarily my parents.
INTERVIEWER: Do you think most people think it is difficult to talk to their parents?
RESPONDENT: Sometimes, because they don't understand.
INTERVIEWER: Are friends better at understanding than parents?
RESPONDENT: Yes, because sometimes they know you better. I don't know why – it's supposed to be the other way around.

The assumption of the role by some teenagers of being a substitute parent is also evident from their accounts, as indicated here by a description of how one girl



STAFFORDSHIRE UNIVERSITY LIBRARY

persuades her friend in a maternal way:

> I help her with her homework if she doesn't understand it. I sort of push her along. She sort of doesn't think. When she was revising she started watching telly and things and really that isn't what you need. So I kind of push her along.

The main source of contact for friends was usually school but social support networks and opportunities for relaxation outside of school and the home were also important for teenagers. For example, scouts were favoured by boys, youth clubs by working-class teenagers, and the pony club by middle-class rural teenagers.

## EMOTIONAL SUPPORT IN THE FAMILY

In the Asian family interviewed, members of the family were included by respondents in their social support network. Shazia, aged 13, referred to her aunt as someone she would go to with a problem, if she felt it was something she could not talk to her parents about:

> No, I don't really go to my friends, if I couldn't go to my mum and dad I'd go to one of my aunties, like Chandra, because she's in the family but she knows, she wouldn't say that it's wrong or what not, she'd go through it all,

A couple of other girls also referred to an aunt as the preferred family member to provide emotional support. Hayley, aged 17, expresses some ambivalence here with an aunt being selected out for some problems (which could cause embarrassment) but with mum in the background for matters which were serious:

RESPONDENT: No, I probably wouldn't even talk to my mum. I would probably talk to my aunty Beverley . . . my mum's a lot older than me or my aunty . . . I'd be too embarrassed to talk about anything (with my mum or dad). . . .
INTERVIEWER: So if you had a really bad problem, who would you go to?
RESPONDENT: My mum.

Other members of the extended family were also sometimes preferred to parents. For example, Ashley, an 18-year-old, would seek advice from his cousins rather than his parents. When they did talk to their family, it was more often to their mother than to their father. In the Asian family interviewed Shazia was the only teenager who clearly stated that she would prefer to go to her father with problems:

> In a way I feel closer to my dad . . . I think I spend too much time with my mum, at the moment my dad's not at work, but when he goes to B—— and I go with him, it's like being away from the home, when we're not at home we don't talk about doing this or that, like my mum does, he talks about all kinds of things, I can talk to my dad about everything, if I've done something wrong my mum will go on at me, but my dad won't even say that I've done it. He'll talk to me . . . but I do get on with both of them, I talk to my mum and dad. . . .

Stephanie, a middle-class 15-year-old, described the differences between her parents and her relationship with them:

> Dad only half listens . . . I don't talk to him about proper things . . . half the things that a man talks about I wouldn't really want to talk to him about.

Teenage girls interviewed generally went to their mother rather than their father to discuss developmental problems as they preferred to talk to someone of the same sex. Even though Shazia preferred talking to her father about her problems, she too preferred to talk to her mother about personal issues:

> It would depend on what the problem was, but I'd prefer to go to my dad; but if it was a girl's personal problem I'd go to my mum probably.

Hayley stated that she talked to her mother about problems now that she is 'grown up', whereas when she was younger she was a 'daddy's girl'. Boys too appeared to prefer to talk about personal and physical problems with their mother rather than with their father.

## BOYS, GIRLS AND EMOTIONS

There appeared to be a gender difference in teenage friendships. Teenage girls had a tendency to reveal to each other more confidential and personal information, for example, about their personal development and emotional problems. This may explain why girls appeared to need a close or best friend whom they could trust – a 'confidante' – and why they found having more than one close friend problematic as it could lead to rivalry and 'bitchiness'. Consequently, some girls reported that they found it easier to talk to boys than girls. Natalie, a working-class 16-year-old, found boys 'less bitchy'. Hayley, another working-class 16-year- old, also found it easier to talk to and make friends with teenage boys:

> With girls they all sit there thinking, 'Oh, am I going to let on to her?' With lads it's different. I just go up to them and go, 'Hiya', and talk to them ... You can tell them anything or have a laugh with them. And if you say something, you think, 'Oh, it doesn't matter'. But if you're talking to girls and you say something they might think, 'Why is she telling me this?' Girls can be a bit more bitchy than lads.

Occasionally boys also differentiated between 'close' or 'best' friends and other friends, especially if they had known each other for a long period of time. Michael, a working-class 13-year-old:

> If I did really badly in an exam and I didn't want anyone to know I'd probably tell my dad ... I probably would tell my best friend but I wouldn't tell them all.

Girls appeared to value having a number of close friends as well as one or more best friends. 'Best friends' usually involved an intimate and at times confiding relationship. 'A best friend is always there for you', as one respondent reported. Another described her friendship as follows:

> I tell my best friend everything, and we do everything together. But my close friends, I might talk to them all the time or see them, but we don't actually go out, I don't tell them everything that has been happening. But I still know I can say things to them all.

The two aspects of close friendship which appear to have particular importance for mental health are: the development of a sense of identity which is separate from that made in relation to family members; and a sense of security derived from group membership. The parent/child bond and closeness still valued by parents are transformed and replaced by friends. Stephanie, a middle-class 15-year-old, described her best friend:

> We're the same height, got the same coloured hair, same kind of writing ... she just makes school kind of special, sort of thing. You have to have the security of knowing that you have a partner for games and you've got someone to sit next to in each lesson and things.

Boys, on the other hand, did not tend to reveal personal matters to their friends, not even to the 'close' or 'best' friends that some of them appeared to have. They also believed that girls talk to their friends more than boys. Indeed, it appears that the majority of teenage boys interviewed did not communicate their personal or emotional problems to anybody – whether friends or family. If these problems were 'big' they might have gone to their mothers, if they were concerned with money they may go to their fathers, as did teenage girls. On rare occasions some of the teenage boys had close relationships, for example with brothers who were close to them in age, or to their mothers if theirs was a single-parent family. On the whole, however, what was striking was how little that teenage boys were prepared to communicate with anybody about emotionality. Whilst (as with the adult respondents) both girls and boys would try to sort their own problems out alone, the desire to do this was much stronger in boys. Ashley, at 18, would sort something out in his own mind:

> Sit down and think about it myself, I don't know, just think about it myself ... I'd do it myself sort of thing if I had a problem ... I wouldn't turn to anybody else, but if it was a big problem like I needed something or I needed a hand with something, I'd go to [his parents], yes.

Tim, from a single-parent family, aged 12, also coped with emotional upsets, such as losing his temper, on his own:

> I just feel like shutting everybody out ... I just go into my bedroom and put my pillow over my head, and I just can't hear anybody else ... I just wait until I've calmed down and then go downstairs.

During their interviews teenage boys were reticent when asked about emotional problems and friendships, for example, Pete, a middle-class 14-year-old:

INTERVIEWER: Is it something you need to talk about with your friends?
RESPONDENT: I probably could do, but it's not our usual conversation.

Steve, a middle-class 16-year-old, was equally reticent:

INTERVIEWER: Do you talk to your friends about things to do with the next stage in your lives, going to University or whatever?
RESPONDENT: Not really.

Paul, a middle-class 13-year-old, who had been bullied at school appeared not to have anybody he felt he could trust to talk to about any of his problems – this was despite his parents encouraging him to talk to them:

INTERVIEWER: What would make life easier for you now, just leave school or ...?
RESPONDENT: Kill everyone.
INTERVIEWER: You mention you've got a couple of friends.

RESPONDENT: Oh yes, but not proper friends.
INTERVIEWER: Do you feel you've ever had any proper friends?
RESPONDENT: No, not really.

He went on to talk about the peer pressure on boys not to show affection to one another:

> You can't have a really close friend if you are a boy ... all they ever talk about is, 'You're a poof you, you're gay', the slightest thing like that.

His teenage sister agreed with this, saying that only girls could hug each other if they were upset, boys could not.

The parents of Liam, a working-class 15-year-old, would tell him to sort his problems out himself rather than offering emotional support, for example, if something happened at school:

> They'd see it from my point of view and then they'd go in to school, if it was something serious they would do but if it's nothing serious they'd just say sort it out yourself.

The difference between boys and girls about the issue of expressing emotions and sharing problems was so striking that it raises questions about the brittle character of emerging masculinity. If boys evade contact with anybody about their inner experiences, it pre-empts the possibility of gaining support from others. In contrast to parents and friends schools were not usually reported as being places from which teenagers were able to derive emotional support. The respondents occasionally alluded to personal and social development lessons at school and were usually dismissive of their worth. For example, Jennifer, a middle-class 15-year old, picked out the reluctance of teachers to become involved when there was a serious problem. She cited the example of a friend who was badly treated at home by her stepfather who had tried to rape her and was regularly beaten up – 'the school knows about it but they've done nothing about it'. In the context of teachers being viewed as lacking in care and concern generally, personal and social development lessons were viewed as just 'another' lesson to mechanically get through.

## FAMILY POSITION AND RELATIONS

Respondents at times alluded to the impact of family position on their relationships. Pauline thought her younger daughter lived in the shadow of her elder daughter, and therefore lacked self-esteem:

> Well, I think it goes back to this thing of a middle child finds it very difficult to know what their identity is ... Joanne (the middle child) is particularly awkward because she ... never really had the time on her own spent with me, I think it's an identity thing and also of all three children she has the lowest self-esteem and I think she requires conflict to establish who she is and what she is.

Being the youngest was also seen as a problem by some respondents. Michael, aged 13, as the youngest, referred to himself as being at 'the bottom of the pile.' Doug, aged 13, said he would like to be the eldest rather than the youngest because he got picked on and shouted at by his elder siblings.

An eldest child was likely to be looked up to by the other children or to be perceived by a parent to be the most dominant child. A middle-class mother, Lisa, referred to her eldest daughter as:

> Quite dominant and she doesn't sort of think to let her younger sister have her time when she gets home ... It's difficult, really, I'm sure I don't do as much as I probably did with the elder daughter.

Paul, aged 13, talked about missing his elder sister Kate, aged 15, when they were younger, when she went on a school trip:

> I slept in her bed and hugged her teddy all week until she came back.

Kate did not miss her younger brother, however:

> When he went away for the first time I thought it was good because he annoyed me ... [he's always] following me around and trying to copy me.

Betty, thought she was closest to her eldest son because he was aged 5 before she had another child:

> He talks to me about absolutely everything, even things that he knows could get him into trouble. We have a trusting relationship.

The number of years between brothers and sisters was also important for some respondents in determining their relationship. Charles talked about his 14-and 16-year-old sons respecting and liking each other:

> They get a great deal of dependence out of each other, and they're very good friends ... the eldest one (21 years old) would see himself as outside that little group, which would heighten the fact that he is on his own really.

The mother in this family, Betty, did not think that the eldest boy, even though he lived at home, talked to his younger brothers:

> I think he talks to them, but not about anything serious or about something that was worrying him.

Another mother, Lisa, thought her daughters got on well, because 'there's a big enough gap so they are not jealous'.

Sometimes the respondents indicated that the sex of the children was also important in determining how well siblings get on with each other. For example, a boy with no brothers and only sisters may be deemed to lose out on emotional support from his siblings. Lisa says:

> I think if I'm there he tends to separate himself off and go into his room and things ... I tend to do things with the girls. Sometimes I feel a bit guilty ... but he doesn't want to come ... but then I think my husband's like that. He's a boy.

By contrast, she thinks that the sisters get on well.

A father found it easier to talk to his son and find hobbies for them both to enjoy:

> I do talk to John, I'll always ask him how he's going on, I follow the football. I ask him what he is doing.

He found it more difficult to be close to his daughters:

> Because they've got other plans, they want to be going out, or they are on the phone, or in the bathroom. So I just check on them to see if they're OK, which is nice I think.

Natalie talked about not knowing her younger brother and hardly ever talking to him, in comparison to her sister:

> I don't really know our John, to tell the truth. We don't really talk much. I go for days without talking to him. Our Joanne, I get on with her a bit.

Changes in family systems also at times affected relationships with teenagers. One woman talked about how her second husband got on less well with his stepdaughter after the birth of his own daughter, and that this led to tensions between the parents as the mother felt protective about her first daughter. Rani, an Asian mother, thought that the Asian culture had presented problems for her daughter as she had grown up and tried to become independent:

> I think it must be awful for her at this stage, to keep a balance with family standards,and what the family expects of you ... I try to keep a happy balance between family life and with her friends, especially now, I always think it's so difficult for them, because of things that aren't acceptable for their culture for a start, for a start boys ... she's at that age, but it won't be acceptable for her to have a boyfriend or something like that ... I think it would be quite stressful if she had to keep it hidden from the family ... she went through a difficult phase, and I think she thought that we didn't understand her, and we didn't know what she wanted ...

However, Shazia, her daughter, talked openly in her interview, about having boyfriends and boys who were close friends when discussing friendships. This was not something she would talk openly about to her parents. Shazia also made some interesting comments about her need to distance herself from her parents and to feel some independence. She talked, for example, about what she would do if in the house on her own.

> ... talking on the phone all day would make me feel good, doing everything different like sitting in your pyjamas all day, not having to look good, not having to go out, not to answer the door, the phone if I don't want to, eating whatever I want to, watching whatever I want to, like being in the house on my own, doing nothing, talking to no one, just being on my own, that would be brilliant. It's just like no hassles, not having to feed the cat, not having to clean its tray out, not having to worry about that mug being in that sink, just being yourself kind of thing.

## THE PLACE OF DISCIPLINE IN FAMILIES WITH TEENAGERS

Methods of disciplining teenagers reported across all types of family included curfews on television watching, expecting children to do small amounts of housework, and depriving them of treats.

Kate and Paul, a middle-class brother and sister, told of the curfew instituted by their father on their television watching:

> Paul. He's got the most pathetic thing at the moment if we . . . I didn't do my homework just once or something so he doesn't let us put the television on from 6 p.m. till 8 p.m., he calls it his 'curfew'!

As with other middle-class children they associated this with parental pressure on them to do well at school. A working-class mother, Clare, who also used this method along with other disciplining methods, did not use it in relation to homework:

> Keeping them in . . . no sweets didn't do her any good . . . so now not watching the video, no telly for the night.

As adolescence comes to an end parents began to attempt to discuss house rules rather than actively disciplining. Ryan, a working-class father, had started to try and talk problems through with his 18-year-old daughter:

> There's been instances where she's not so much come to me, but I've gone to her and I find out things and I say 'OK, let's approach this in a mature manner now, which is the best way to go, how do you feel about this?' On this particular occasion she was a bit gobsmacked, actually.

Though surprised, he believed she was pleased with this change in attitude and had responded positively to this change in their relationship.

Shouting was another disciplinary method cited by parents. Julia, a working-class mother, said that if there was a problem her husband shouted, to 'put the fear of God into them'. Jenny, another working-class mother, thought her husband could be excessive when he taunted their teenage children, but she accepted this form of discipline as necessary in the hostile environment in which they lived:

> Like sometimes I think that he's a bit cruel with some of things he says to them, but he's trying to bring them out a bit . . . to see how they react, because he knows this is what they'll get outside the house.

Clare, a working-class mother, referred to punishment as something to use on younger children:

> Keeping them in. We did try it with [my daughter] when she was a lot younger, keeping her in for a week, and then it went to a fortnight.

Paul, a working-class father reported, 'mine are grounded every other day, it's just the first thing that comes out of my mouth'.

Physical punishment of teenagers was another form of discipline used. In our sample this did not appear to be related to class type, nor was it only fathers who administered physical punishment. Ashley, a working-class 18-year-old, referred to his mother's use of physical punishment, as opposed to his father's:

> She'll take a run at me and batter me with a shoe or something like that, my dad just laughs about it. Even if I argue with my dad . . . my mum will get up and hit me.

Lisa, a middle-class mother, referred to her non-use of physical punishment, 'I don't actually hit them'. However, she went on to explain that one of the reasons for her not doing was that she was frightened that her son might retaliate. Another middle-class mother, Viv, admitted she would slap the younger children, but, punishing the older children in this way tended to induce feelings of guilt. Most people who used physical punishment were of the opinion that it was not harmful provided that the physical force used was minimal. As one man put it, 'they get the occasional backhander, but don't get a belting'.

The establishment of ground rules about homecoming can be considered another form of discipline which was evident in the accounts. Parents in working-class families (who mainly lived in urban areas) reported being strict about stipulating homecoming times for their teenage children, as they were fearful of what could happen to their teenagers outside the home, especially after dark. Parental worry about crime and violence centred around the threat of sexual violence in relation to girls, especially if they were coming home alone after dark; boys were deemed to be more at risk of physical violence such as mugging, fighting and stabbing. Hostile and dangerous environments were major themes in many of the interviews with working-class parents (one working-class son was given an attack alarm by his parents, because they were so worried about him). This contrasted with parental and teenage accounts from semi-rural areas where fear of crime and violence was less and boundaries about coming and going less stringent.

## WORKING-CLASS FAMILY CONCERNS AND RISK-TAKING BEHAVIOUR

In working-class families, including the Asian family interviewed, the main concerns for parents were their lack of a future and the illicit drugs and the violence that they felt were prevalent in their neighbourhood, especially if they lived in an urban area. Julia, a working-class mother, thought her teenage children worried about drugs, AIDS and jobs. She was much more concerned about the effect on her teenage children of the contemporary economic situation than any of the middle-class parents interviewed:

> What are they going to do with their lives? Are they going to be in jobs? Are they going to be able to go to college? Are they going to be able to afford to live and eat?

A mother (Marjorie), said her main concern was about her teenage children at school:

> Anyone picking on them ... and letting her go to town on her own, knowing that there is thugs out there who could pick on her.

A father (Paul), worried about local gang violence:

> I think they've now got the problems of gangs of kids fighting, I mean we had them but it wasn't an everyday thing. I mean if you got a black eye ... you didn't get your ribs broken or your head knocked off.

Michael, 13-years-old, was frightened by the violence in his neighbourhood:

> I won't go to the shops because there's always big gangs hanging around there and I'm not too keen ... They could just come and mug you or beat you up, like my mate was walking down the road the other day and three lads just jumped out at him, one hit him in the head and one winded him ... I live in a very rough area.



UNIVERSITY LIBRARY

The link was also made between drugs, alcohol and violence on some council estates:

> I know there's a lot of drugs round here. I know from police officers . . . I was going to say I know but let's say from word of mouth, that there's lots of it, if you want it you can get it. Without any problem . . . There's a certain part on the estate where you can virtually get it . . . A lot of them, if you see the state of some of the kids on Fridays and Saturdays . . . I don't know if they're [drinking alcohol] and taking drugs, but they're very violent with it.

Teenagers were more able to give an opinion about 'risk-taking' behaviours such as drugs, crime and sexual relations than they were about issues to do with emotionality. Not surprisingly opinions about drug-taking differed considerably. One teenager reported being 'shocked' to see his cousin taking cannabis at a family party whilst another reported the same drug to be 'just like a strong cigarette'. This latter respondent also considered that 'Manchester is probably a cannabis-smoking population . . . And Whiz [amphetamine], I think a lot of people have that when they go to clubs'. One respondent admitted to having had a serious drinking problem which she considered had had a profound impact on her life. She reported having been almost expelled from college due to non-attendance when she felt too drunk and ill to get up in the morning:

> Life was going downhill and I thought, 'Right I'm going to do something about it', so I did . . . We could have done with going to Alcoholics Anonymous, it was that bad. [Drinking] just started off as something to do, and then it got more and more, and then it got ridiculous . . . People drink to try to block problems out . . . and if you're under pressure. . . .

Opinions about suicide were less freely given than opinions about risk-taking behaviours which people presumably had more day-to-day experience of. Most people reported 'never thinking about it'. Where it was mentioned, it was attempted rather than actual suicide that respondents talked about. The cause of attempted suicide was usually linked to relationship problems with sexual partners – especially at the point where relationships had broken up. In reporting that one of his schoolmates had tried to commit suicide, one young teenager implies that attempted suicide may also produce some cultural capital by reporting it to be commonplace and 'an OK thing to do':

> Well, in school it's like an OK thing, this lad's tried committing suicide when he was younger, and there's other people that have done it . . . [because of] girls and their parents.

Concerns on the part of teenagers about parental problems were not confined to discussions about suicide but was a more general theme in teenagers' accounts, particularly in families with two parents. Perhaps, therefore, the greater impact of divorce on teenagers rather than on younger children has not been sufficiently acknowledged and this may be an issue worthy of further study. For example, Doug, a working-class 13-year-old, related teenage suicide to divorce:

> If they've got any problems at home, like their parents arguing, going through a divorce or something like that. . . . There was one person, his mum and dad got a divorce, and someone asked him if he wanted to talk about it, and he just went hysterical. It must have really affected him.

In relation to the issue of conformity, teenage respondents, particularly from working-class families, reported feeling pressured by peers to buy fashionable clothing. Poorer children and their parents, in particular, appeared to feel pressurised to buy 'the right' material goods. Ashley, a working-class 18-year-old, stated:

> You see your mate with a nice shirt on, one about eighty quid . . . and I'd say I'll get one of them. But all my mates spend a lot of money on clothes and it makes you think, 'I'll buy that'.

## BULLYING

Conforming seemed to be the opposite side of the coin to bullying, of which working-class children had more direct experience: difference results in bullying. Kelly, a working-class 17-year-old, thought:

> . . . you get bullied if you're just a geek, no social life, then they get picked on. I think the quiet ones get picked on a lot more, than if you was in with a crowd.

Ashley thought his classmate was bullied because:

> . . . there was something weird about him, he was dead nervous and that, so people bullied him and that made him worse, I could see it.

Warren, a middle-class 12-year-old, felt those who were bullied were those with physical differences, who spoke differently, such as a boy in his class who had a deep voice as well as being new to the area.

## MIDDLE-CLASS FAMILY CONCERNS AND RISK-TAKING BEHAVIOUR

Middle-class parents worried much less about such issues as drugs or violence. They were more likely to be concerned with, and to presume that their teenagers were concerned with, developmental problems. Celia, a middle-class mother, thought the main teenage problems were:

> Growing up – emotional, sexual maturity. She seems to be coping OK, I think there's a lot of hormonal . . . that starts earlier, but she seems to have gone very quickly like . . . she's got a boyfriend, a steady boyfriend.

One father (Peter), listed teenage problems as:

> . . . trying to cope with institutional life in schools, forming human relationships . . . trying to cope with a rather defensive and hostile world. . . . I'm at a loss really to how you define mental health in teenagers, I find that very difficult.

Middle-class teenagers' problems appeared to be less pressing and extreme than those of their working-class counterparts. Stephanie, a 15-year-old, when asked if she ever got worked up about things and felt unable to cope, admitted her main personal worry came from her babysitting job:

> Well, over this week I've been babysitting for somebody . . . she would tell me things about our governors and things and that was really stressful, and her

> children wouldn't go to bed at the right time ... and then she didn't pay me, I thought I'm doing all this for her and she didn't even pay me.

She saw the question of issues that she faced as a teenager in depersonalised terms, probably related to what she had learnt at school, listing these as:

> euthanasia ... abortion ... genetic screening, not genetic engineering ... I don't think that's right, being a Christian.

Another mother (Betty), felt her main worry was what other people might think if her children did not do well academically:

> If you do well at O levels you can do A levels and then go on to university, I think there's pressures to do well and people judge people a lot more on how well they've done academically.

When asked if the drug culture of the city in which her son attended university worried her, she answered, 'No, I don't think it did, I only worry about them doing well at school'.

## EDUCATION AND TEENAGERS

Education was one of the main concerns of parents in relation to their teenagers' lives, development, success, and mental health. For teenagers themselves school was an important source of emotional support through friendships (for girls but not boys), but also of stress, as it caused worries in both the short-term in relation to examinations, and in the long-term in relation to employment and careers. Many teenagers spoke about problems when starting secondary school in finding friends and being in a strange environment. Although adjustments to school life appeared to be alleviated to an extent if a child had a peer or sibling who already attended a particular school. Steven, a middle-class 16-year-old, for example stated, 'it wasn't so bad because my older brother was at the same school'.

## CLASS DIFFERENCES AND EDUCATION

More working-class teenagers (and those of lone parents) wanted to leave school and find employment in order to earn money than those from middle-class backgrounds. Their parents, in turn, were worried about their prospects of finding work. Hayley, a working-class 16-year-old, did worry about doing well at school, and against her parents' wishes had decided to break with tradition and return to education in order to go to university, as her elder brother had done. She was, however, worried about the debts she might have to run up:

> Like my brother was shouting at my mum, 'Make her go back to school'. But I think my mum wanted me to stay on at my job. My dad definitely wanted me to stay on at my job. But I knew that I wanted to take my A levels really.... I'm thinking about going to university, but then I'm thinking, 'No, have you seen the state of my brother, what's it going to do to me?' And he's got loads of debt....

In families where there were few expectations about teenagers going on to higher education or doing well academically there appeared to be little pressure from parents or tension about the undertaking of homework.

Whilst pressure to do homework or perform well academically did not feature extensively in working-class childrens' accounts, middle-class children were, it seems, expected to go to university and sometimes felt pressurised by parents and school to be successful academically. Kate talked about the pressure she felt she was under:

> Pressure from exams and stuff . . . especially when you get into fourth year . . . and you think, 'Shut up and go away'. I don't really care right now . . . they pressurise you all the time.

Betty, a middle-class mother, talked about listening to her teenagers whilst admitting that she still felt it legitimate for education to be one of her main concerns and to therefore pressurise her son to continue his education against his wishes:

> . . . yes, I do think about it a lot because it's important that the children do well academically. . . . Whatever he wants to do, I listen, but I want him to go back to university.

One of the main concerns of Martin, a middle-class father, in relation to his teenage children was their academic success, 'Getting through her GCSEs . . . the rest is just normal growing up. That's imposed by us, on them.'

## THE FINDINGS ON TEENAGERS IN RELATION TO OTHER RESEARCH

In the context of the finding that the adolescent period is characterised by little class variation in health (West, 1988; West *et al.*, 1990), intra-familial differences relating to family functioning, family culture and parenting styles have recently been considered as more important than examining variations between socio-economic groupings (Parker, 1983; Brannen *et al.*, 1994). Family conflict has been identified as being a major variable that affects the health and well-being of teenagers (Sweeting and West, 1995). For example, Rutter and Smith (in Moore, 1995) point to an increasing amount of conflict and tension in families with teenage children arising from several concurrent issues: the increasing social isolation of teenagers from their parents; teenagers' financial dependence on their parents for longer periods; and the emphasis in modern society on individual consumption and gratification. Teenagers are thus encouraged by society to be individual consumers, but their economic position denies them access to such financial independence.

Economic deprivation still plays an important role, however, in determining teenagers' mental health (Rutter and Smith in Moore, 1995). Thus, as with the epidemiology on adult mental health problems, a class gradient exists but is largely accounted for by the correlation between psychopathology and poverty. Those from the poorest of the lower-class social groupings (i.e. not all working-class people) are at most risk.

## FAMILY FUNCTIONING

Lundberg (cited in Sweeting and West, 1995) found that two variables representing family 'dysfunction', a broken family in early family life and conflicts in the family, were important in terms of impact on health, including the mental health of teenagers. These variables were found to be more important than economic variables. Sweeting and West (1995) found that family functioning was a more important variable in determining the health of teenagers than family type or structure and in those families which are more 'family-centred', teenagers were found to have better relationships with their parents. Psychological and social effects of disruption in the family appear to have more of a significant negative impact on the psychological health of adolescence than on younger children and in single-parent rather than reconstitutedfamilies (Hetherington and Clingempeel, 1992).

In the research literature there is a consensus that conflictual relationships between teenagers and their parents have negative consequences. It has been associated with low self-esteem, delinquency, depression, poor psychological adjustments and para-suicidal behaviour (Sweeting and West, 1995). In our study evidence points to the importance of considering the *meaning* of constructs such as family-centredness and conflict. It may be remembered from Chapter 5 that not all conflict is seen as negative and is dependent on whether the effects of conflict are seen as having a positive or negative outcome. Notions of familial closeness also varied substantially.

## ECONOMIC DEPRIVATION

Despite the stress laid in recent research on family dysfunction, economic variables have still been seen as important by some commentators. Economically deprived teenagers – those who were working class, poor, unemployed, or council estate tenants – are 'more likely to be criminal, depressed, suicidal and addicted to drugs than those in more comfortable circumstances (Rutter and Smith in Moore, 1995). As we noted above, to be working class is probably not in itself a vulnerability factor but it becomes so if combined with variables such as poverty, unemployment and other factors noted below.

## RISK-TAKING BEHAVIOUR AND CONFORMITY

Rutter and Smith (in Moore, 1995) listed as likely teenage stressors: parental marital breakdown, prolongation of education and its concomitant risk of failure and rejection, the availability of drugs and pressure to conform over drugs and alcohol, and the traditional pressures of adolescent sexuality. When referring to the social and emotional identity of the contemporary teenager, they also emphasise the contribution made by the importance laid in the past decade on the philosophy of the free market, individual gratification and consumption. This plays an important part in the extension of peer pressure to include the buying and owning of certain fashion items, which are often expensive. This pressure was felt especially strongly by children and parents from families with the least ability to purchase such items. In our study, pressure to conform and the need to be seen to consume fashionable clothes was in evidence amongst teenagers from working-class families in urban areas suffering from economic deprivation, although the link between this and mental health in lay accounts was not obvious. In relation to smoking and the consumption of alcohol Brannen *et al.* (1994, p. 142) noted a gender difference between the behaviour expected by parents of teenage girls and teenage boys – girls' parents were strict about alcohol, and boys' parents about smoking. In this study, parents did not appear to make such gendered distinctions, being concerned about the teenagers of either sex being involved with cigarettes or alcohol.

## FAMILY CULTURE

Family culture in research is often related to notions of: the extent of family activity, family cohesiveness, support and affection, parenting styles and family roles, relationships and responsibilities, and disciplining methods. Most research in this area suggests a relationship between family cohesiveness and self-esteem in adolescents. Parenting style which tends to cut across class boundaries (Hetherington and Clingempeel, 1992) is also associated with certain effects on teenagers' mental health. For example, authoritative parenting as opposed to permissiveness or authoritarianism has been associated with the social competence and adjustment of teenagers (Baumrind, 1978). Affectionless control (low care with high protection) has been associated with a higher risk of neurotic disorders (Parker, 1983). Rutter and Smith (in Moore, 1995), too, argue that teenage mental illness is linked less to family breakdown/dysfunction than to family culture, i.e. there being less parental support and involvement. The research reported here suggests that assumptions and definitions about many of these core constructs are highly variable both between and within family types. Notions of familial 'culture' also tend to ignore the structural and environmental context in which norms,values and beliefs are shaped and therefore, we would argue, need to be interpreted with caution.

## GENDER DIFFERENCES, 'TALKING RELATIONSHIPS' AND EMOTIONAL SUPPORT

Brannen *et al.* (1994, p. 205) have argued that a gender difference exists between the relations of mothers and fathers to their teenage offspring. Mothers (but not fathers) 'see it as their task to create a "talking relationship" with their children' whilst fathers seek to forge a new tie with their teenage children through 'a joking relationship which attempts to smooth away status differences'. Our research confirms the finding that teenagers are more likely to discuss problems with their mothers and that mothers, more than fathers, take care to foster this role and are responsible for rule-making in the home. Daughters especially are more likely to talk to their mothers about personal or developmental problems.

Whilst gender differences may be evident between communicative styles of parents, recent research has found little evidence to suggest that the *impact* of familial factors on teenage mental health and well-being is gendered. It has been noted that 'the absence of sex differences is surprising in view of the different biological and maturational factors involved and the gendered nature of roles within the family' (Sweeting and West, 1995). Sweeting and West did find, however, that a link could be established between the presence of conflict in a family and the greater negative effect this had on girls' health and self-esteem in both the short and long terms, compared to boys (p. 169).

Phoenix (1991, pp. 134–5) found in a survey of young mothers when looking at their social support networks a reticence to disclose personal information. In our study we find the same about teenagers (and adults) not wanting to confide in others. Offer and Kimberley (1992). It has also been argued that some adolescents may prefer to handle problems by themselves or seek some sort of informal help, and more rarely they may seek the assistance of a professional in health or education. Young women interviewed in this study reported that friends might not be trustworthy and that ideally they were looking for a 'confidante'. What they underline, however, is that confidentiality is the key factor in attaining and maintaining this sort of help-seeking by a teenager with emotional problems. Finally, the findings of this study have drawn attention to gender difference in relation to the emotional support sought in friends and family. Girls appear to look for confidentiality in a close friend to whom they will reveal personal information whilst boys prefer to try and solve problems on their own.

## IMPLICATIONS FOR MENTAL HEALTH PROMOTION

- Given the importance attributed by teenagers to their peers compared to adults, parents, teachers and health professionals need to recognise particular sensitivities about negotiating trust and openness with teenage children. Jacobson and Wilkinson (1994), referring to GP contact with teenage patients, argue that fostering an atmosphere of adolescent centredness is central to reducing psychological morbidity. Of significance here are teenagers with low self-esteem who are less likely to seek the help. If confidence is to be inspired about the ability to deal with serious problems such as bullying, pregnancy, or risk-taking behaviour, teachers and health professionals need to listen when they are approached for help with apparently trivial problems. From our study this would mean health professionals acknowledging that there is a preference for non-disclosure and self-reliance as coping mechanisms and for disclosing to peers amongst teenage girls. It has been pointed out that teenagers may not discuss problems with health professionals for the same reasons they do not communicate with parents (Brannen *et al.*, 1994).
- The role of friendship and social networks in teenagers is important to teenagers. An example of this would be to see teenagers themselves as being the main resource to reduce bullying in schools through co-counselling schemes. The provision of such support would need to take into consideration the different and gendered systems of social contact and support which teenagers engage with.
- Given the reticence about disclosure and a preference for self-reliance, responding empathically and seriously to problems which are disclosed and maintaining confidentiality is likely to be central to those adults who seek to provide emotional support and help to teenagers seeking help (Offer and Kimberley, 1992). Teachers and others in contact with teenagers need to ensure that they do not minimise or gloss over problems which are disclosed. Given that it is probable that these communications only occur after the teenager has struggled with their personal diffidence, any disclosure should be taken seriously. The weak confidence expressed about personal and social development lessons suggests that these are not sufficiently efficient or credible in the eyes of pupils to take the place of personal support and counselling.
- Health professionals, health promoters and teachers need to be particularly aware of the emotional difficulties of teenage *boys* and the poor chance of them expressing personal problems. Informal networks are important here to some extent in alleviating these problems, but evidence in this study suggests that even here boys may find less emotional support than girls. From this study we do not know whether or not the higher suicide rate among young men is determined in part by this gender difference in disclosure. However, it is clear that the greater personal isolation of teenage boys may be a vulnerability factor.
- Although Sweeting and West (1995) mentioned the negative aspects of conflict on teenagers' adjustment and self-esteem, theirs was a quantitative study and did not elaborate on people's views of conflict and whether it had a detrimental effect. Our study therefore complements theirs as respondents clearly differentiated between positive and negative views in relation to conflict. Some respondents saw conflict as beneficial whereas others saw it as harmful. Health promotion strategies need to reflect this complexity. For example, teachers acting

as mental health promoters or counsellors, would be advised to check the specific meaning a teenager attributes to conflict during any dialogue rather than relying purely on professional or disciplinary notions.

- Discussion of parenting skills and child discipline in health promotion literature needs to take on the 'hidden' agenda of power and parents need to be made more aware that psychological issues to do with power and emotions might shape or underlie attitudes to discipline. Parental views about discipline may simply appear to be explicit rationales about child-rearing. However, they may also be implicit rationales to protect parental power over their children and justifications for the expression of aggression in the family.
- Health promotion about a number of health topics mentioned that caused anxiety for both parents and their teenage children, such as drug misuse and AIDS, can be seen to have a wider *mental* health implication. Information and discussion about these topics need to take into account their emotional connotations.

# 8. Views about social background

It is evident from the data discussed in previous chapters that there are not clear-cut differences between the views of respondents from different social classes. Some trends have been present but so has an overlap between classes and variations within them. Also people between and within roughly the same occupational and financial circumstances varied in the way in which they construed others. However, there did seem to be a stronger consensus about single parents from those who were not in this social group.

In general those who were not single parents themselves viewed being a single parent as presenting a whole range of difficulties in terms of managing on one's own. In relation to other aspects of the data, what stands out about the views about single parents is the assured way in which people felt able to express an opinion about this group in society and the certainty with which they construed the 'problem' of being a single parent. Occasionally this 'expertise' was underpinned by reference to statistics or analysis reported in newspapers. Single parents were usually seen in stereotypical terms. Those who were not single parents typically did not consider that single parenthood might be a positive choice or that it may not be a problem. Single parents were considered by their very nature to be less supported emotionally and financially. Rarely, was single parenthood viewed as a transient state. Single parents were generally viewed as poor, starting as teenagers with young babies and staying that way. Lone parents did not see themselves in the way others did, as can be seen from the data already discussed about emotional support. For them class differences were more striking than whether they were single parents or not.

### *A consensus note on the dangers of a designer culture*

A further paradox related to the way in which families with children who were highly conscious of fashion were viewed. Whereas fashion-conscious teenage families themselves believed that conspicuous consumption was a social marker of success and well-being, those with less overt materialism – from both working-class and middle-class families – viewed having very expensive trainers and chic clothes in a poor light. These onlookers considered that a designer culture reflected badly on family values.

For example, one working-class teenager's view of 'all those kids that are in fashion all the time' was that 'their families will be more rough like "go and get it yourself"'. By this he meant that they would be uncaring and aggressive. Similar views could be found in accounts from people of a variety of backgrounds in which the acquisition of expensive trainers, shaved heads and attention to fashion were viewed as markers not of success but of delinquency and low social class.

## POVERTY, WEALTH AND SOCIAL CLASS

We have noted already in Chapter 2 'Lay epidemiology' that a strong consensus existed in the data about social determinism across class backgrounds. The first set of vignettes cited below reinforce this point. However, within this broad consensus there were mixed or even contradictory viewpoints. Some people viewed money as a cushioning factor against mental distress, as indicated by this middle-class respondent about working-class people:

> I think the threat of or actual redundancy or the sack can cause problems. Working-class people are already living at the lowest level of redundancy. It creates problems because it is not as if they can share things.

He goes on to say that for middle-class people the experience of redundancy:

> ... would be just as upsetting but they have got more leverage, generally they have a better educational standard and this enables them to analyse things more deeply. I think they have more options open to them.... The media says that middle-class people drink more when they are under a lot of pressure but I am not sure that this is the correct view.

And when asked whether people from different social class backgrounds experienced the same sort of stresses as people from this man's social class, which was working class, he apparently had no doubts about the connection and responded:

> Have they hell! Money opens doors. It buys better health, that's been well proved. They say money can't buy health but by hell it helps.

The connection between money and being able to maintain mental health was also not lost on this respondent who commented about richer people's problems in relation to her own in this way:

> Well they don't have money problems, do they, and more of ours are money problems ... if you have money you can sort a lot of the stresses out of day-to-day living. You'd have more holidays for a start. I think holidays are a good way of unwinding. I'd like to have more than one a year.

Even when amounts of money were not actually the issue, control and middle-class resources were seen as having a cushioning effect against the impact of stress. Here a middle-class women expresses this view in relation to a television programme:

> There was a programme on the telly, children saying they couldn't have the things they wanted. A lot of the things they said they wanted my children don't have. They don't have things like ... I get trainers from BhS and things, I don't get the 'right' trainers. But that doesn't make me feel bad. Even if I had the money I wouldn't get them everything new. So it's like sort of being in control. We have more choice and we're more in control [than working-class people].

At times metaphors about poverty were used with reference to the environment of those deemed to be in a low social class as indicated by this male secondary school teacher who talks about the families that some of his pupils come from:

> I mean in the area that I teach you see an awful lot of very unhappy children – all kinds of poor family backgrounds. I don't mean poor financially, poor in terms of neglect and abuse and beatings. I would imagine those kids will find it very difficult to overcome the trauma they have suffered ... because for them a sense of normality doesn't correspond with what we think of as normal family background. They have no stability at all.

However, there were other ways in which wealth and its link to happiness and emotional stability were construed which was the counterpart to relative poverty – relative richness. The presence as well as the scarcity of money was deemed to be problematic for some. In this regard, the 'politics of envy' are notable by their absence. Social scientists have often used the concept of relative deprivation to describe a situation where poverty is viewed not as an absolute construct but something in which material wealth is seen relative to accepted norms about desirable items in a society, and relative to those with wealth and power. Similarly 'stress' and emotional difficulties can be seen as relative to the circumstances and norms of wealthy people's lives.

We also noted at the end of Chapter 2 that, subjectively, people judge themselves relative to their self-defined social reference group. This can lead to judgments about one's own reference group and assumptions about other social groups. An extreme example of the latter was one unemployed respondent who thought that richer people would still (like him and his partner) argue about limited resources but in the rich couple's case it would be over 'whether the wife wanted a tiara'. Some saw those who were financially better off than themselves as merely facing different problems from themselves rather than questioning the degree of experienced stress – 'theirs [their problems] might not be about the holiday. It might be another car'.

This working-class respondent viewed the problems of those in steady and well paid employment as different in this way:

> They have a different type of stress, peer pressure and outside influences, like your children mixing with people who you consider they shouldn't mix with . . . I don't suppose people like Princess Diana would like the idea of her children mixing with different social groups.

Here a mother from the position of a public sector middle-class family talks of other families who attend the same private school as her children:

> Most of the parents there will earn considerably more money than we do and the women tend not to work. But they tend to have husbands doing very stressful jobs. I think if you're self-employed it's more stressful because you don't know what you're going to earn at the end of the year. So they get the good side of having a high standard of living. But they get the bad side of more stress.

Interestingly some people who were in these more affluent categories *did* report some of these problems identified emphatically by those in lower social positions. Stress was also viewed by a significant number of respondents from different class backgrounds as a universal construct, for example, 'Stress is different but the same'.

## IMPLICATIONS FOR MENTAL HEALTH PROMOTION

- If the stereotypical views of single parents found in this research are evident in the wider population then the key problem lone-parent families are likely to face in relation to mental health is the stigma attached to them from other groups who predominantly view their social status in problematic and negative terms. In this regard mental health promoters might do well to reflect the variegated and ordinary way in which single parents view themselves.
- There appears to be a strong consensus on stress and class, confirming the views set out in the Chapter 2 on lay epidemiology, but we also noted that the

respondents considered that stress exists in all social classes, with its attributed source varying from one class to another. Three points can be made about this.

First, the belief from poorer people that the rich have problems too could be a cognitive strategy to reduce their sense of dissonance about their own social position (in addition to recognising that people from all social classes experience mental health problems). Such a reduction in dissonance was also evident in the ways in which some single parents argued about their own status.

Secondly, studies of mental health across the classes have demonstrated that people from all walks of life *do* suffer stressful life events. However, richer people have a greater ratio of buffering or mitigating positive experiences to these negative events than do poorer people (Myers, 1975). A confirming finding about this is that mental health scores improve in old age for the rich but deteriorate within poorer groups (Blaxter, 1990).

Thirdly, the lay assumptions about abuse in childhood transcending class boundaries are confirmed by existing empirical evidence, especially in relation to sexual abuse.

These three points could account for an apparent inconsistency in the range of responses given. The attributions made by respondents about the existence of stress and abuse in all social classes is not inconsistent with their overall consensus that poverty, work stress and job insecurity are the main determinants of mental health problems. As with the professional discourse about social determinism it is credible to argue *both* that a class gradient and other predictable differences exist, between social groups in mental health, *and* that individuals in all groups can have problems. Thus, the implications for mental health promotion are the same for this chapter as for the one on lay epidemiology. People would find messages acceptable that are in tune with their assumptions about social determinism and individual differences within overall trends of disadvantage.

# References

Antonovsky, A. (1979) *Health, Stress and Coping.* San Francisco and London: Jossey-Bass.
Backett, K. (1987) *The Achievement of Health – the Middle Classes discuss Health in Families.* Working Paper 13. Research Unit in Health and Behavioural Change, University of Edinburgh.
Backett, K.C. (1990) Studying health in families: a qualitative approach, in Cunningham-Burley, S., and McKeganey, N.P. (eds) *Readings in Medical Sociology* London and New York: Tavistock and Routledge.
Backett, K. (1992) Taboos and excesses: lay health moralities in middle class families. *Sociology of Health and Illness* **14**(2), 255–75.
Baumrind, D. (1978) Parental disciplinary patterns and social competence in children. *Youth in Society* **9**, 239.
Bergin, A. and Garfield, S. (1994) *Handbook of Psychotherapy and Behaviour Change,* London: Wiley.
Blaxter, M. (1990) *Health and Lifestyles.* London: Routledge.
Brannen, J. (1995) Young people and their contribution to household work. *Sociology* **29**(2), 317–38.
Brannen, J., Dodd, K., Oakley, A., and Storey, P. (1994) *Young People, Health and Family Life.* Milton Keynes: Open University Press.
Broverman, D., Clarkson, F. Rosenkrantz, P., *et al.* (1970) Sex role stereotypes and clinical judgements of mental health. *Journal of Consulting and Clinical Psychology* **34**, 1–7.
Brown, G.W. and Harris, T. (1978) *Social Origins of Depression.* London: Tavistock.
Cooke, K. (1987) The living standards of unemployed people. In Fryer, D. and Ullah P. (eds), *Unemployed People: Social and Psychological Perspectives.* Milton Keynes: Open University Press.
Cornwell, J. (1984) *Hard-earned Lives: Accounts of Health and Illness from East London.* London: Tavistock.
Davison, C., Davey-Smith, G., and Frankel, S. (1991) Lay epidemiology and the prevention paradox: the implications of coronary candidacy for health education. *Sociology of Health and Illness* **13**, 1–20.
de la Cuesta, C. (1993) Fringe work: peripheral work in health visiting. *Sociology of Health and Illness* **15**(5), 663–82.
Department of Health (1992) *The Health of the Nation: a Strategy for Health in England,* Cm 1986. London: HMSO.
DeSwaan, A. (1990) *The Management of Normality,* London: Routledge.
Dingwall, R. and Robinson, K. (1990) Health visiting and the public surveillance of private behaviour. In Gubruim, J. and Sarhar, A. (eds), *The Home Care Experience: Ethnography and Policy.* London: Sage.
Duncombe, J. and Marsden, D. (1993) Love and intimacy: the gender division of emotion and emotion work. *Sociology* **27**(2), 221–41.
Edwards, J. (1995) 'Parenting skills': views of community health and social service providers about the needs of their clients. *Journal of Social Policy* **24**(2), 237–59.
Fabrega, H. and Manning, P.K. (1972) Disease illness, and deviant careers. In Scott R.A., and Douglas J.D. (eds), *Theoretical Perspectives on Deviance.* New York: Basic Books.
Fabrikant, B. (1974) The psychotherapist and the female patient: perceptions and change. In

Franks, V. and Burtle, V. (eds.), *Women in Therapy*. New York: Brunner Mazel.
Fenton, S. and Sadiq, A. (1991) *Asian Women and Depression*. London: Commission for Racial Equality.
Field Institute (1984) *In Pursuit of Wellness: a Survey of Californian Adults*. Sacramento: California Department of Health.
Finch, J. and Mason, J. (1993) *Negotiating Family Responsibilities*. London: Tavistock/ Routledge.
Fryer, D. (1995) Benefit agency? Labour market disadvantage, deprivation and mental health – the 1994 CS Myers Lecture. *The Psychologist* 8(6), 265–72.
Glaser, B. and Strauss, A. (1971) *The Discovery of Grounded Theory: Strategies for Qualitative Research*. Chicago: Aldine.
Goffman, E. (1968) *Asylums: Essays on the Social Situation of Mental Patients and Other Inmates*. Harmondsworth: Penguin.
Graham, H. (1994) *When Life's a Drag: Women, Smoking and Disadvantage*. London: HMSO.
Hetherington, E., and Clingempeel, W. (1992) Coping with marital transitions: a family systems perspective. *Society for Research in Child Development Monographs*, vol. 57, pp. 2–3.
Hill, F. (1988) *Mental Health Education: Where Do We Start?* Studies in Education. London: Westminster Health Promotion Unit.
Hochschild, A.R. (1983) *The Managed Heart: Commercialisation of Human Feeling*. London: University of California Press.
Horwitz, A. (1983) *The Social Control of Mental Illness*, New York: Academic Press.
Irwin, S. (1995) Social reproduction and change in the transition from youth to adulthood. *Sociology* 29(2), 293–315.
Jacobson, D. (1989) Context and the sociological study of stress: an invited response to Pearlin. *Journal of Health and Social Behaviour* 30, 257–60.
Jacobson, L.D. and Wilkinson, C.E. (1994) Review of teenage health: time for a new direction. *British Journal of General Practice* 44, 420–4.
Jacobson, L., Wilkinson, C., and Owen, P. (1994) Is the potential of teenage consultations being missed? A study of consultation times in primary care. *Family Practice* 11(3), 296–9.
Jahoda, M. (1958) *Current Concepts of Positive Mental Health*. New York: Basic Books.
James, A. (1989) Emotional labour. *Sociological Review* 37, 15–42.
James, A. (1992) Care = organisation + physical labour + emotional labour. *Sociology of Health and Illness* 14(4), 489–509.
Jones, L. and Cochrane, R. (1981) Stereotypes of mental illness: a test of the labelling hypothesis. *International Journal of Social Psychology* 27, 99-107.
Matthews, K., Milne, S., and Ashcroft, G. (1994) Role of doctors in the prevention of suicide – the final consultation. *British Journal of General Practice* 44(385), 345–8.
Mirowsky, J. and Ross, C. (1989) Psychiatric diagnosis as reified measurement. *Journal of Health and Social Behaviour* 30, 11–25.
Moore, S. (1995) Stressed out on life. *Guardian*, 1 June.
Myers, J. (1975) Life events, social integration and psychiatric symptomatology. *Journal of Health and Social Behaviour* 16, 121–7.
Newton, J. (1992) *Preventing Mental Illness in Practice*. London: Routledge.
Oakley, A. (1974) *The Sociology of Housework*. London: Martin Robertson.
Oakley, A. (1988) Is social support good for the health of mothers and babies? *Journal of Reproductive and Infant Psychology* 6, 3–21.
Oakley, A. and Rajan, L. (1991) Social class and social support: the same or different? *Sociology* 25, 1.
Oakley, A., Rigby, S., and Hickey, D. (1994) Life stress, and class inequality: explaining the health of women and children. *European Journal of Public Health*4, 81–91.

Offer, D. and Kimberley, A. (1992) Debunking the myths of adolescents: findings from recent research. *Journal of the American Academy of Child and Adolescent Psychiatry* **31**, 6.

Parker, G. (1983) Parental Overprotection: *a Risk Factor in Psychosocial Development.* New York: Grune & Stratton.

Pearlin, L. (1989) The sociological study of stress. *Journal of Health and Social Behaviour* **30**, 241–56.

Phoenix, A. (1991) *Young Mothers.* Cambridge: Polity Press.

Pilgrim, D. and Rogers, A. (1993) Mental Health service users' views of medical practitioners. *Journal of Interprofessional Care* **13**, 129–48.

Pilgrim, D. and Rogers, A. (1994) Something old, something new ... sociology and the organisation of psychiatry. *Sociology* **28**(2), 521–38.

Pill, R., and Stott, N. (1982) Concepts of illness causation and responsibility: some preliminary data from a sample of working class mothers. *Social Science and Medicine* **22**, 1347–54.

Popay, J., Bartley, M., and Owen, G. (1993) Gender inequalities in health: social position, affective disorders and minor physical morbidity. *Social Science and Medicine* **36**(1), 21–32.

Roberts, H., Smith, S and Bryce, C. (1993) Prevention is better... *Sociology of Health and Illness* **15**, **447-63**.

Rogers, A., Pilgrim, D., and Lacey, R. (1993) *Experiencing Psychiatry: Users' Views of Services.* London: Macmillan.

Rose, N. (1990) *Governing the Soul: the Shaping of the Private Self.* London: Routledge.

Schaefer, C., Coyne, J.C., and Lazarus, R.S. (1981) The health related functions of social support. *Journal of Behavioural Medicine* **4**, 381–406.

Scheff, T. (1966) *Being Mentally Ill: a Sociological Theory.* Chicago: Aldine.

Scheper-Hughes, N. (1990)

Sedgwick, P. (1980) *Psychopolitics.* London: Pluto Press.

Stern, J., Murphy, M., and Bass, C. (1993) Attitudes of British psychiatrists to the diagnosis of somatization disorders. *British Journal of Psychiatry* **162**, 463–6.

Sweeting, H., and West, P. (1995) Family life and health in adolescence: a role for culture in the health inequalities debate. *Social Science and Medicine* **40**, 2, 216–221.

Szasz, T.S. (1961) *The Myth of Mental Illness.* New York: Harper & Row.

Warr, P., and Payne, R. (1983) Social class and reported changes after job loss. *Journal of Applied Social Psychology* **13**, 206–22.

Watson, J. (1993) Male body image and health beliefs: a qualitative study and implications for health promotion practice. *Health Education Journal* **52**, 4, 246–52.

West, P. (1988) Inequalities? Social, class differences in health in British Youth. *Social Science and Medicine* **27**, 2, 91–96.

West, P., Macintyre, S., Annandale, E., and Hunt, K. (1990) Social class and health in youth: findings from the West of Scotland Twenty 00–7 Study. *Social Science and Medicine* **30**, 665.

Wheelan, C.T. (1993) The role of social support in mediating the psychological consequences of economic stress. *Sociology of Health and Illness* **15**(1), 86–102.

Whiting, B., and Whiting, J. (1975) *Children of Six Cultures.* Cambridge, Mass.: Harvard University Press.

## APPENDIX D:
## PUBLICATIONS – HEA FAMILY HEALTH RESEARCH PROGRAMME

The following titles are available as part of the above series and can be ordered through Marston Book Services, telephone 01235 465565.

Hogg., C., Barker, R., and McGuire, C. (1996) *Health Promotion and the Family: Messages from Four Research Studies*. HEA.
Holland, J., Mauthner, M., and Sharp. S. (1996) *Family Matters: Communicating Health Messages in the Family*. HEA. (Original working title: The Family Health Natural History Project.)
Brannen, J., and Storey, P. (1996) *Child Health in the Social Context: Parental Employment and the Start of Secondary School*. HEA.
Rogers, A., and Pilgrim, D. with Latham, M. (1996) *Understanding and Promoting Mental Health*: A Study of Familial Views
Prout, A. (1996) *Families, Cultural Bias and Health Promotion: Implications of an Ethnographic Study*. HEA.

**Forthcoming**

Beattie, A. *et al* (1996) *Family Health and Housing Poverty*. HEA.
Brynin, M., and Scott, J. (1996) *Young People Health and the Family: Results from the British Household Panel Study*. HEA.
Sharpe, S., and Mauthner, M., and France-Dawson, M., (1996) *Families, Communication and Health: A Literature Review*. HEA.

04334676